CORRECTION REQUESTED < < <
1 94599GDS97&BX 3 NADZ 8

1 A GOOSEFF
VETRANS HOME STATN
POBX 97 VET HOME
YOUNTVILLE CA 94599

$4.30
S0-BDQ-192

Selected Solutions for

PHYSICS Part I, Third Edition

by

Robert Resnick and David Halliday

prepared by

Edward Derringh
Department of Physics
Rensselaer Polytechnic Institute

John Wiley & Sons, Inc.
New York · Santa Barbara · London · Sydney · Toronto

This material may be reproduced for
testing or instructional purposes by
people using the text.

ISBN 0 471 02444 9
Printed in the United States of America

10 9 8 7 6 5 4

CONTENTS

CHAPTER 1

1-6

(a) 1 light-year = (186,000 mi/s)(3.156 X 10^7 s) = 5.87 X 10^{12} mi or

$$1 \text{ mi} = \frac{1}{5.87 \times 10^{12}} = 0.17 \times 10^{-12} \text{ ly.}$$

Therefore

$$1 \text{ A.U.} = 92.9 \times 10^6 \text{ mi} = 92.9 \times 10^6 \text{ mi} \times 0.17 \times 10^{-12} \text{ ly/mi}$$

$$= 15.8 \times 10^{-6} \text{ ly } \underline{\text{Ans.}}$$

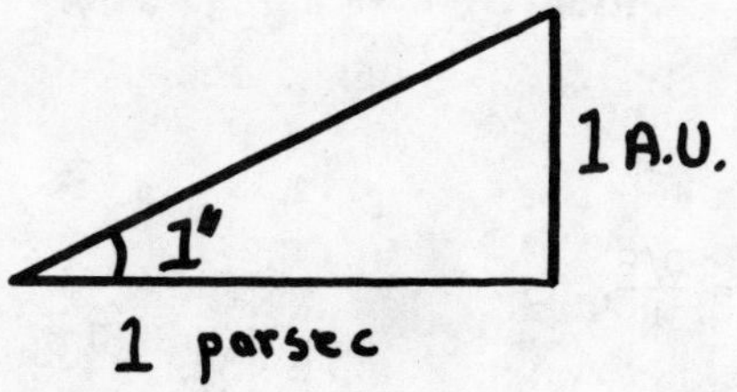

Since 206265 " = 1 rad,
206265 A.U. = 1 pc,
and

$$1 \text{ A.U.} = \frac{1}{206265} \text{ pc}$$

$$= 4.85 \times 10^{-6} \text{ pc } \underline{\text{Ans.}}$$

(b) From (a), 1 ly = 5.87 X 10^{12} mi Ans.

Since 1 A.U. equals 4.85 X 10^{-6} pc and 15.8 X 10^{-6} ly, it follows that

$$4.85 \text{ pc} = 15.8 \text{ ly},$$

$$1 \text{ pc} = 15.8/4.85 = 3.26 \text{ ly.}$$

Therefore,

$$1 \text{ pc} = (3.26)(5.87 \times 10^{12} \text{ mi}) = 19.1 \times 10^{12} \text{ mi } \underline{\text{Ans.}}$$

1-9

The apparent angular diameters α of the sun and moon in the sky are virtually identical. Thus the situation at total eclipse is practically as shown in the figure. Let $\overline{ab} = r$, $\overline{ac} = R$.

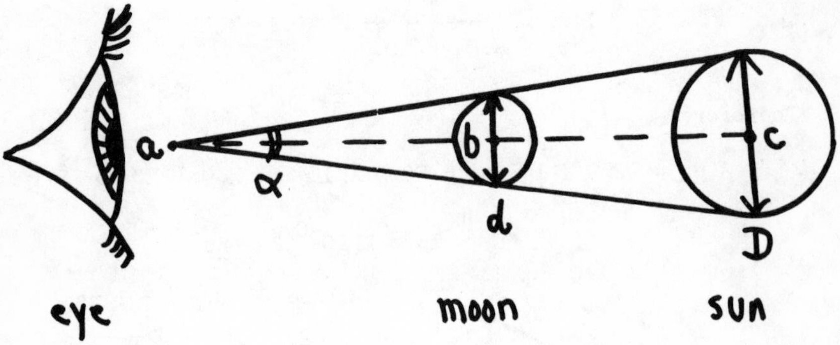

(a)

$$\sin(\alpha/2) = \frac{d/2}{r} = \frac{D/2}{R},$$

which gives

$$D/d = R/r = 400\, r/r = 400 \text{ Ans.}$$

(b) Vol of sun/Vol of moon = $D^3/d^3 = (400)^3 = 6.4 \times 10^7$ Ans.

(c) In the figure, substitute dime for moon, and moon for sun. You will find by experiment that α is about 9.2×10^{-3} rad (i.e. you must place a dime about 190 cm from your eye to just eclipse the sun or moon; do NOT try this experiment with the sun). The average earth-moon distance R is 3.8×10^5 km. Since $\alpha \ll 1$,

$$D = R\alpha = (3.8 \times 10^5 \text{ km})(9.2 \times 10^{-3}) = 3500 \text{ km Ans.}$$

1-10

From Table 4: proton mass = 1.7×10^{-27} kg,
electron mass = 9.1×10^{-31} kg.

Therefore the mass of a hydrogen atom is

$$(1.7 \times 10^{-27} + 9.1 \times 10^{-31})\text{ kg}$$

$$= 1.70091 \times 10^{-27}\text{ kg},$$

and

$$1\text{ kg} = \frac{1}{1.70091 \times 10^{-27}}\text{ hydrogen atom masses}$$

$$= 5.9 \times 10^{26}\text{ hydrogen atom masses } \underline{\text{Ans.}}$$

1-12

(a) $1\text{ g/cm}^3 = 10^{-3}\text{ kg}/10^{-3}\,\ell = 1\text{ kg}/\ell$ Ans.

(b) 1.0 liter of water contains 1.0 kg, from (a). Since

$$10\text{ hours} = 10\text{ h} \times 3600\text{ s/h} = 36 \times 10^3\text{ s},$$

the mass flow rate is

$$1.0\text{ kg}/36 \times 10^3\text{ s} = 2.8 \times 10^{-5}\text{ kg/s } \underline{\text{Ans.}}$$

1-18

The last day of the twenty centuries is longer than the first day by

$$(20\text{ centuries})(10^{-3}\text{ s/century})$$

which is 0.020 s. The average day during the twenty centuries is (0 + 0.020)/2 = 0.010 s longer than the first day. Since the increase occurs uniformly, the total cumulative effect is

$$\Delta T = (\text{avg. difference})(\text{No. of days})$$

$$= (0.010\text{ s/avg. day})(365.25\text{ days} \times 2000)$$

$$= 7305\text{ s} = 2.0\text{ h } \underline{\text{Ans.}}$$

1-22

(a) The 'radius' of a proton is 10^{-15} m, and the radius of the observable universe is about 10^{26} m. The logarithmic mean of these is $10^{(26 - 15)/2} \doteq 10^{5.5}$, or between 10^5 and 10^6 meters Ans.

(b) Log (pion lifetime) = log(2) - 16 = 0.3 - 16 = -15.7.
The age of the universe = $(4 \times 10^9 \text{ yr})(3.15 \times 10^7 \text{ s/yr})$ $= 12.6 \times 10^{16}$ s. Since $\log(12.6 \times 10^{16}) = 17.1$, the required time interval is $10^{(17.1 - 15.7)/2} = 10^{0.7} = 5$ s Ans.

CHAPTER 2

2-3

If X,Y coordinate axes are placed on the figure as shown, the head of the vector $\vec{r} = \vec{a} + \vec{b}$ will be found somewhere on the circle of radius b, the precise location depending on the angle θ between $\vec{a}$ and $\vec{b}$.

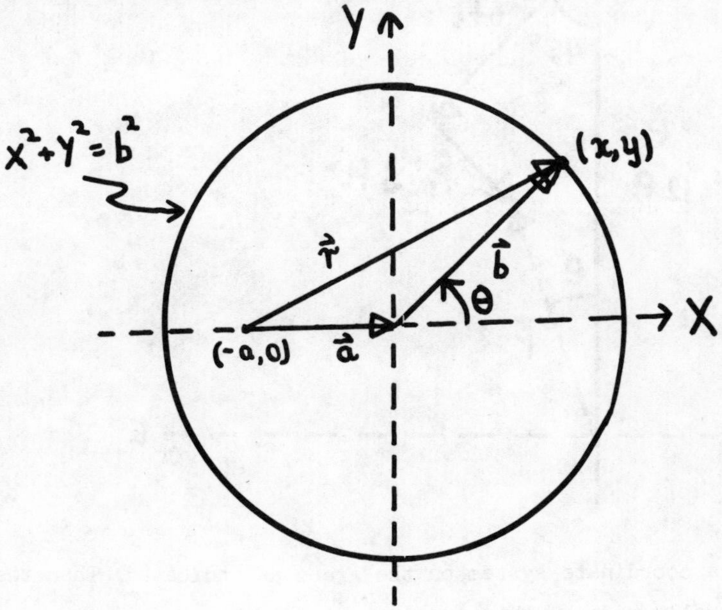

We have

$$r = \sqrt{[x - (-a)]^2 + (y - 0)^2}$$

$$= \sqrt{a^2 + b^2 + 2ax} \ ,$$

since $x^2 + y^2 = b^2$. Now $-b \leqslant x \leqslant b$ and therefore

$$r_{min} = a - b, \text{ or } b - a, \quad \text{whichever is} > 0.$$

This occurs when x = -b, in which case $\theta = \pi$. Similarly,

$$r_{max} = a + b;$$

here x = +b, $\theta = 0$.

2-5

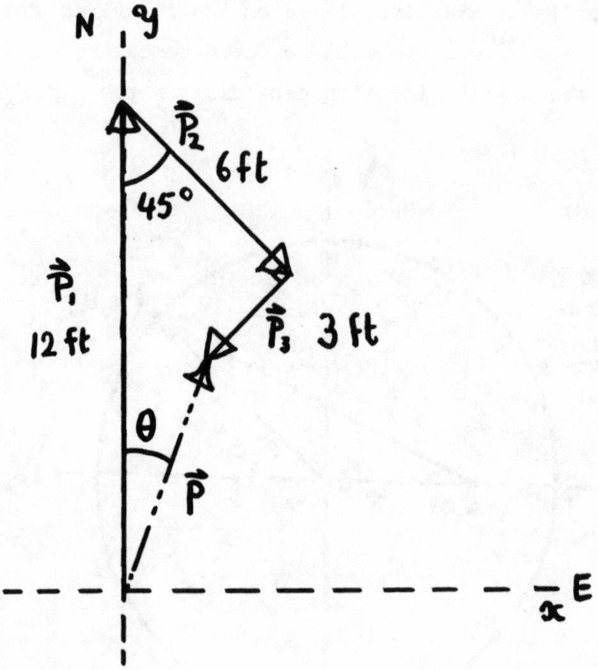

Place a coordinate system on the green as indicated. Then the putts actually made by this incompetent golfer were

$$\vec{p}_1 = 12\,\vec{j};\quad \vec{p}_2 = 6\frac{\sqrt{2}}{2}\,\vec{i} - 6\frac{\sqrt{2}}{2}\,\vec{j};\quad \vec{p}_3 = -3\frac{\sqrt{2}}{2}\,\vec{i} - 3\frac{\sqrt{2}}{2}\,\vec{j}.$$

The single putt needed to sink the ball was

$$\vec{p} = \vec{p}_1 + \vec{p}_2 + \vec{p}_3 = 2.12\,\vec{i} + 5.64\,\vec{j},$$

of which the magnitude and direction are

$P = 6.0$ ft; $\Theta = \sin^{-1}(2.12/6.0) = 20.5^{\circ}$ East of North Ans.

2-10

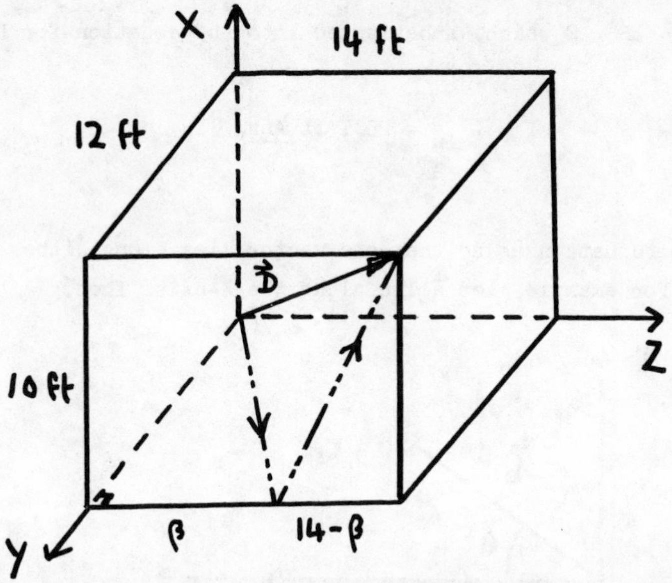

(a) From the figure, $\vec{D} = 10\,\vec{i} + 12\,\vec{j} + 14\,\vec{k}$, and therefore

$$D = \sqrt{(10)^2 + (12)^2 + (14)^2} = 21 \text{ ft Ans.}$$

(b) Answering the questions in turn:

it is difficult to see how;

yes: fly need not fly in a straight line;

yes: it could fly in a straight line (rather unlikely).

(c) For the room as oriented above and choice of corners indicated,

$$\vec{D} = 10\,\vec{i} + 12\,\vec{j} + 14\,\vec{k} \text{ Ans.}$$

(d) The length L of the walked path shown in the figure is

$$L(\beta) = \sqrt{(12)^2 + \beta^2} + \sqrt{(14 - \beta)^2 + (10)^2}.$$

To find the smallest L set

$$\frac{dL}{d\beta} = 0;$$

this gives $\beta = 168/22$ which, substituted into the equation for $L(\beta)$ yields

$$L_{min} = 26.1 \text{ ft } \underline{\text{Ans.}}$$

2-12

Orient the coordinate axes so that one vector lies along either the X or Y axis: for example, let $\vec{a}$ lie along the X-axis. Then,

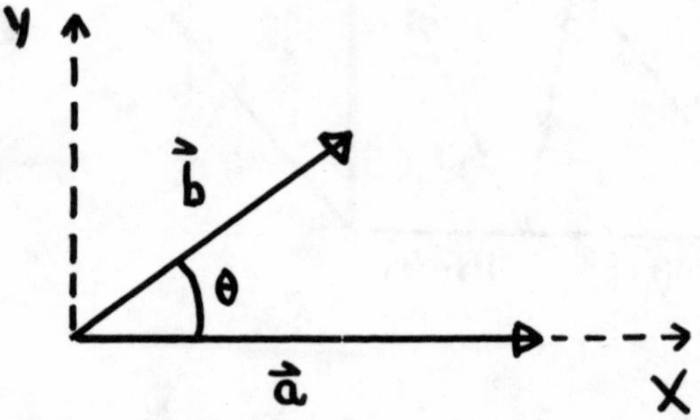

$$\vec{a} = a\,\vec{i};\ \vec{b} = b\cos\theta\,\vec{i} + b\sin\theta\,\vec{j},$$

and we have

$$\vec{a} + \vec{b} = (a + b\cos\theta)\vec{i} + b\sin\theta\,\vec{j},$$

$$|\vec{a} + \vec{b}| = \sqrt{(a + b\cos\theta)^2 + (b\sin\theta)^2} = \sqrt{a^2 + b^2 + 2ab\cos\theta} \text{ } \underline{\text{Ans.}}$$

2-17

Colatitude of Washington = $90^\circ - 39^\circ = 51^\circ$;

Colatitude of Manila = $90^\circ - 15^\circ = 75^\circ$.

(a) The displacement vector $\vec{D}$ joins Washington and Manila along the straight line joining them through the solid earth, and points toward Manila Ans.

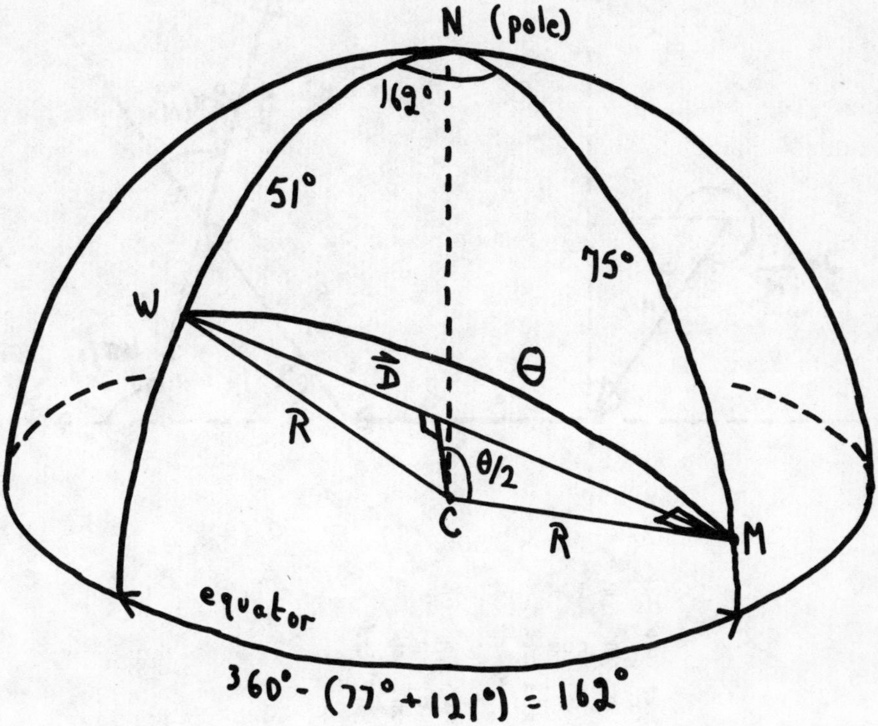

In the spherical triangle NMW,

$$\cos\Theta = \cos 51^\circ \cos 75^\circ + \sin 51^\circ \sin 75^\circ \cos 162^\circ = -0.55105.$$

If R = 6378 km, the radius of the earth, it is clear from the plane triangle WCM that

$$D = 2R \sin\frac{\Theta}{2} = 11,230 \text{ km } \underline{\text{Ans}},$$

using the value of Θ from the previous equation.

2-19

Presented in the next figure are the first and last vectors of the chain of N vectors. Aligning the coordinate axes as shown it is evident that

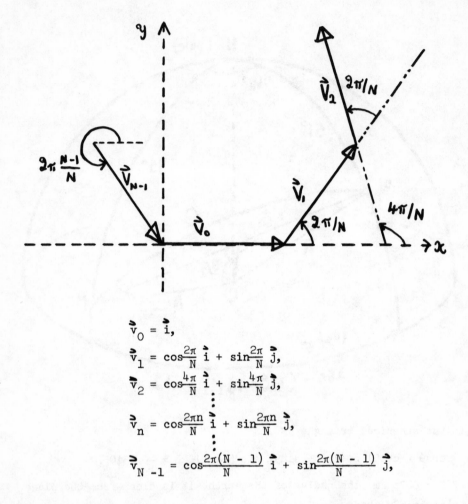

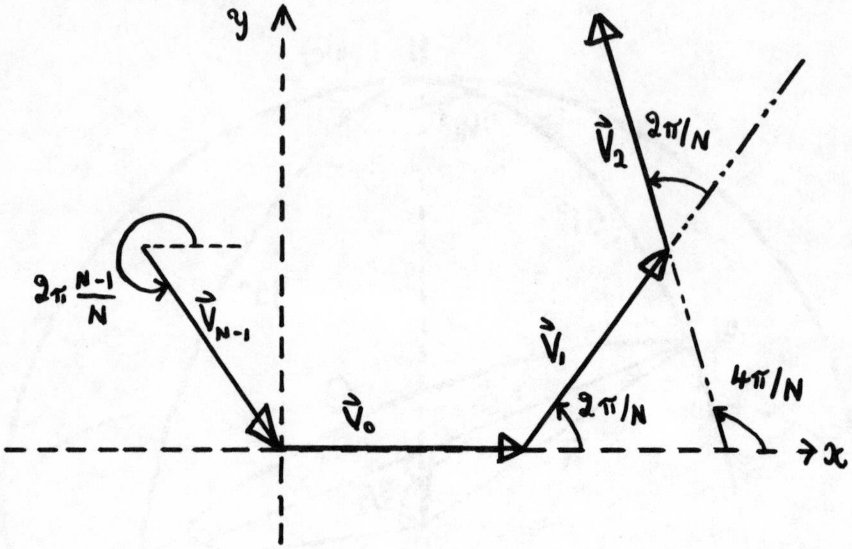

$$\vec{v}_0 = \vec{i},$$

$$\vec{v}_1 = \cos\frac{2\pi}{N}\,\vec{i} + \sin\frac{2\pi}{N}\,\vec{j},$$

$$\vec{v}_2 = \cos\frac{4\pi}{N}\,\vec{i} + \sin\frac{4\pi}{N}\,\vec{j},$$

$$\vdots$$

$$\vec{v}_n = \cos\frac{2\pi n}{N}\,\vec{i} + \sin\frac{2\pi n}{N}\,\vec{j},$$

$$\vdots$$

$$\vec{v}_{N-1} = \cos\frac{2\pi(N-1)}{N}\,\vec{i} + \sin\frac{2\pi(N-1)}{N}\,\vec{j},$$

all the vectors being considered as of unit length.

Clearly, the vectors form a polygon of N equal sides: that is,

$$\sum_{n=0}^{N-1} \vec{v}_n = 0\,\vec{i} + 0\,\vec{j}.$$

But, taking components of the individual vectors, it is easily seen that this last quantity is also given by

$$\left[1 + \cos\frac{2\pi}{N} + \cos\frac{4\pi}{N} + \dots + \cos\frac{2\pi(N - 1)}{N}\right]\vec{i}$$

$$+\left[0 + \sin\frac{2\pi}{N} + \sin\frac{4\pi}{N} + \dots + \sin\frac{2\pi(N - 1)}{N}\right]\vec{j}.$$

Thus the terms in the square brackets must vanish identically. But we can write

$$1 = \cos 0,\ 0 = \sin 0,$$

and we have

$$\sum_{n=0}^{N-1} \cos\frac{2\pi n}{N} = \sum_{n=0}^{N-1} \sin\frac{2\pi n}{N} = 0.$$

2-26

(a) $\vec{a}\cdot\vec{b} = ab\cos\sphericalangle(\vec{a},\vec{b}) = (10 \text{ units})(6 \text{ units})\cos 60^\circ = 30 \text{ units}^2$

(b) $|\vec{a} \times \vec{b}| = ab\sin\sphericalangle(\vec{a},\vec{b}) = (10 \text{ units})(6 \text{ units})\sin 60^\circ = 52 \text{ units}^2$;

The direction of the vector is perpendicular to the plane containing $\vec{a}$ and $\vec{b}$.

2-29

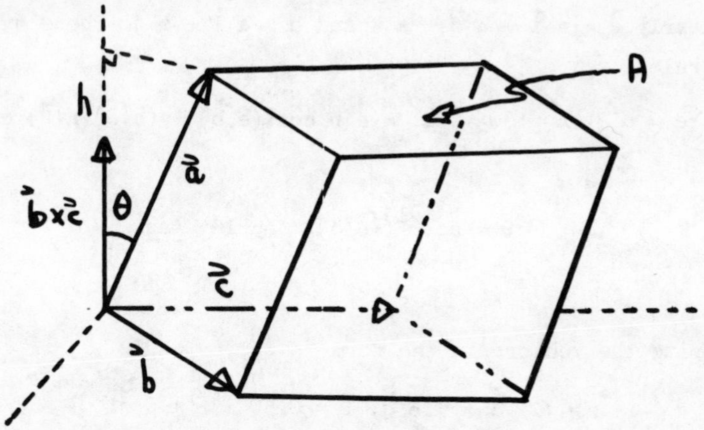

$$|\vec{b} \times \vec{c}| = \text{area of base} = \text{area of top} = A,$$

$$a \sin\theta = h.$$

Therefore,

$\vec{a}\cdot(\vec{b} \times \vec{c}) = a|\vec{b} \times \vec{c}| \sin\angle(\vec{a}, \vec{b} \times \vec{c}) = a\ A \sin\theta = (a \sin\theta)A = hA,$

which is the volume of the parallelepiped.

2-34

By straightforward calculation we find:

(a) $\vec{B} \times \vec{C} = -8\,\vec{i} + 5\,\vec{j} + 6\,\vec{k},$

$\vec{A}\cdot\vec{B} \times \vec{C} = -8(3) + 5(3) + 6(-2) = -21$ Ans.

(b) $\vec{B} + \vec{C} = \vec{i} - 2\,\vec{j} + 3\,\vec{k},$

$\vec{A}\cdot\vec{B} + \vec{C} = 3(1) + 3(-2) - 2(3) = -9$ Ans.

(c) $\vec{A} \times (\vec{B} + \vec{C}) = (3\,\vec{i} + 3\,\vec{j} - 2\,\vec{k}) \times (\vec{i} - 2\,\vec{j} + 3\,\vec{k})$

$= 5\,\vec{i} - 11\,\vec{j} - 9\,\vec{k}$ Ans.

2-35

(a) $\vec{b} = a\,\vec{i} + a\,\vec{j}$ and $\vec{c} = a\,\vec{j} + a\,\vec{k}$. Then,

$$\vec{d} = \vec{b} \times \vec{c} = a^2(\vec{i} + \vec{j}) \times (\vec{j} + \vec{k}) = a^2(\vec{i} \times \vec{j} + \vec{i} \times \vec{k} + \vec{j} \times \vec{j} + \vec{j} \times \vec{k}) = a^2(\vec{k} - \vec{j} + 0 + \vec{i}) = a^2\,\vec{i} - a^2\,\vec{j} + a^2\,\vec{k}$$ Ans.

(b) $\vec{b}\cdot\vec{c} = a.0 + a.a + a.0 = a^2$ Ans.

$\vec{d}\cdot\vec{c} = \vec{d}\cdot\vec{b} = 0$ since $\vec{b} \times \vec{c}$ is perpendicular to both $\vec{b}$ and $\vec{c}$ Ans.

(c) Clearly $\vec{e} = a\,\vec{i} + a\,\vec{j} + a\,\vec{k}$ and $\vec{b} = a\,\vec{i} + a\,\vec{j}$. Then, by the usual rules,

$$\vec{b}\cdot\vec{e} = a^2 + a^2 + 0 = 2a^2 = e\ b \cos\angle(\vec{e}, \vec{b}) = (a\sqrt{3})(a\sqrt{2}) \cos\theta$$

so that

$$\theta = \cos^{-1}(\sqrt{6}/3) = 35^\circ\,16'$$ Ans.

2-37

(a) Write the vectors in the form

$$\vec{A} = 3.2\,\vec{i} + 1.6\,\vec{j};\ \vec{B} = 0.50\,\vec{i} + 4.5\,\vec{j}.$$

Then,

$$\vec{A}\cdot\vec{B} = (3.2)(0.50) + (1.6)(4.5) = 8.8 = A\ B \cos\theta.$$

Since

$$A = \sqrt{(3.2)^2 + (1.6)^2} = 3.58; \quad B = \sqrt{(0.5)^2 + (4.5)^2} = 4.53,$$

we have

$$8.8 = (3.58)(4.53)\cos\theta$$
$$\theta = \cos^{-1}(0.543) = 57° \ \underline{\text{Ans.}}$$

(b) Let $\vec{C} = C_x\vec{i} + C_y\vec{j}$. If $\vec{C}$ is perpendicular to $\vec{A}$, $\vec{C}\cdot\vec{A} = 0$. Also, $C = 5$. Thus we have two simultaneous equations:

$$0 = C_x(3.2) + C_y(1.6);$$
$$\sqrt{C_x^2 + C_y^2} = 5.$$

Solving gives

$$C_x = \pm 2.24; \quad C_y = \mp 4.48 \ \underline{\text{Ans.}}$$

2-39

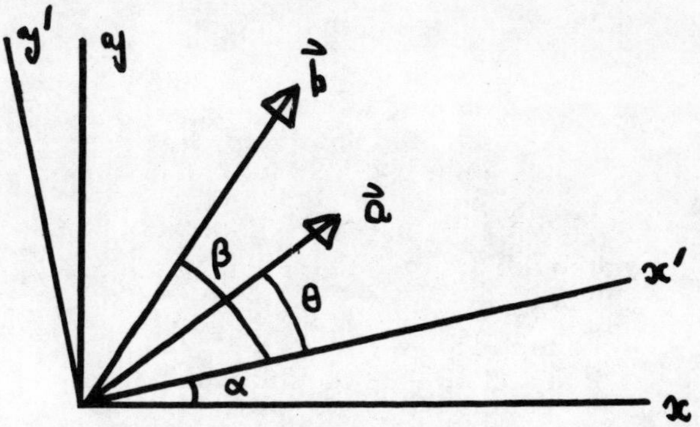

The vectors $\vec{a}$ and $\vec{b}$ expressed in the two coordinate systems are

$$\vec{a} = (a\cos\theta)\vec{i}' + (a\sin\theta)\vec{j}' = a\cos(\theta + \alpha)\vec{i} + a\sin(\theta + \alpha)\vec{j};$$
$$\vec{b} = (b\cos\beta)\vec{i}' + (b\sin\beta)\vec{j}' = b\cos(\beta + \alpha)\vec{i} + b\sin(\beta + \alpha)\vec{j}.$$

We also have relations between the unit vectors:

$$\vec{i}' = \cos\alpha\,\vec{i} + \sin\alpha\,\vec{j};$$
$$\vec{j}' = -\sin\alpha\,\vec{i} + \cos\alpha\,\vec{j}.$$

Therefore

$$(\vec{a} + \vec{b})' = (a \cos\theta + b \cos\beta)\vec{i}' + (a \sin\theta + b \sin\beta)\vec{j}'$$
$$= (a \cos\theta + b \cos\beta)(\cos\alpha\ \vec{i} + \sin\alpha\ \vec{j})$$
$$+ (a \sin\theta + b \sin\beta)(-\sin\alpha\ \vec{i} + \cos\alpha\ \vec{j})$$
$$= \left[a(\cos\theta \cos\alpha - \sin\theta \sin\alpha) + b(\cos\beta \cos\alpha - \sin\beta \sin\alpha)\right]\vec{i}$$
$$+ \left[a(\cos\theta \sin\alpha + \sin\theta \cos\alpha) + b(\cos\beta \sin\alpha + \sin\beta \cos\alpha)\right]\vec{j}$$
$$= \left[a \cos(\theta + \alpha) + b \cos(\beta + \alpha)\right]\vec{i}$$
$$+ \left[a \sin(\theta + \alpha) + b \sin(\beta + \alpha)\right]\vec{j}$$
$$= \vec{a} + \vec{b} \text{ in unprimed system.}$$

CHAPTER 3

3-4

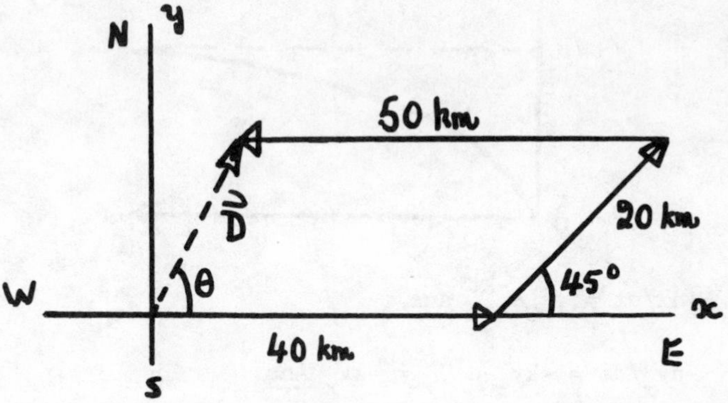

Let $\vec{D}$ = the train's displacement during the total travel time T. Then, by definition, the average velocity $\bar{\vec{v}}$ is

$$\bar{\vec{v}} = \vec{D}/T.$$

From the figure $\vec{D}$ is easily seen to be

$$D = \left[40\,\vec{i} + (20\frac{\sqrt{2}}{2}\,\vec{i} + 20\frac{\sqrt{2}}{2}\,\vec{j}) - 50\,\vec{i}\right] \text{ km}$$

$$= 4\,\vec{i} + 14\,\vec{j}$$

using $\sqrt{2} = 1.4$.

Obviously

$$T = 40 \text{ min} + 20 \text{ min} + 50 \text{ min} = \frac{11}{6} \text{ h}.$$

Since $D = \sqrt{4^2 + 14^2}$, the magnitude and direction of the average velocity are

$$\bar{v} = \frac{14.6 \text{ km}}{11/6 \text{ h}} = 8 \text{ km/h},$$

$$\theta = \tan^{-1}(14/4) = 73\tfrac{1}{2}^{\circ},$$

or in a direction $90^\circ - 73\frac{1}{2}^\circ = 16\frac{1}{2}^\circ$ E of N <u>Ans.</u>

<u>3-10</u>

(a) Note that $x(0) = 0$, $x(\infty) = v_{x0}/k$.

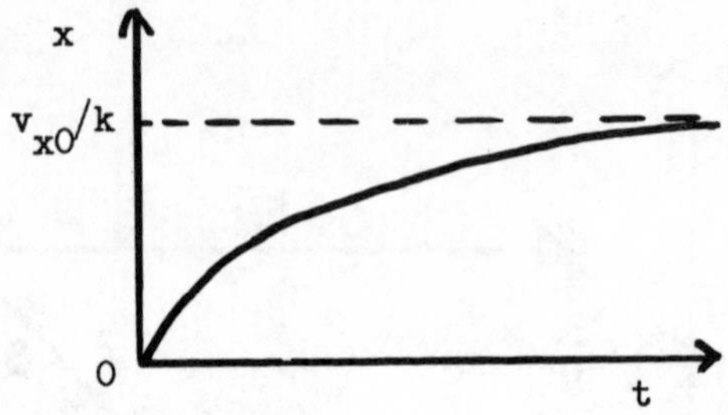

(b) $v_x = dx/dt = v_{x0}e^{-kt}$ <u>Ans.</u>

(c) $a_x = dv_x/dt = -kv_{x0}e^{-kt} = -kv_x$ <u>Ans.</u>

(d) By (c), the acceleration diminishes as fast as the velocity; i.e. at small velocities, the tendency of the velocity to become smaller is itself small.

<u>3-18</u>

The stopping distance s and the assumed maximum possible deceleration a are

$$s = 19.2\ \text{ft};\ a = 32\ \text{ft/s}^2.$$

Then, the car's greatest possible possible initial speed v was

$$v^2 = 2\,a\,s = 2(19.2\ \text{ft})(32\ \text{ft/s}^2) = (35\ \text{ft/s})^2,$$

or v = 24 mi/h. The car's speed could not have been greater than this for, if it was, it would have taken more than 19.2 ft to bring the car to a halt (the <u>maximum</u> deceleration was used above).
<u>Not Guilty</u>.

3-26

Let the vehicle be moving at a speed v_0 when, at t = 0, the driver slams on the brakes a distance s from the barrier, which it strikes 4.0 s later and at a speed of v_f. Then, if a is the acceleration, and since 56 km/h = 15.57 m/s,

(a)
$$s = \frac{1}{2} a t^2 + v_0 t + s_0,$$

$$35 = \frac{1}{2} a 4^2 + (15.57)4 + 0,$$

giving

$$a = -3.4 \text{ m/s}^2 \quad \underline{\text{Ans.}}$$

(b)
$$v_f = v_0 + a t = 15.57 + (-3.4)(4)$$

$$v_f = 2.0 \text{ m/s} \quad \underline{\text{Ans.}}$$

3-28

Let t = reaction time, t' = breaking time at 50 mi/h, and $\tilde{t}$ = the breaking time at 30 mi/h. Then, if a is the deceleration, and since 30 mi/h = 44 ft/s and 50 mi/h = 73.3 ft/s,

$$(73.3)t + \frac{1}{2} a t'^2 = 186,$$

$$(44)t + \frac{1}{2} a \tilde{t}^2 = 80,$$

and

$$73.3 = a t'; \; 44 = a \tilde{t}.$$

Thus we have four equations for the four unknowns a, t, t', $\tilde{t}$. Solving simultaneously gives

(a) t = 0.74 s Ans.

(b) $-a$ = acceleration = -20 ft/s^2 Ans.

3-29

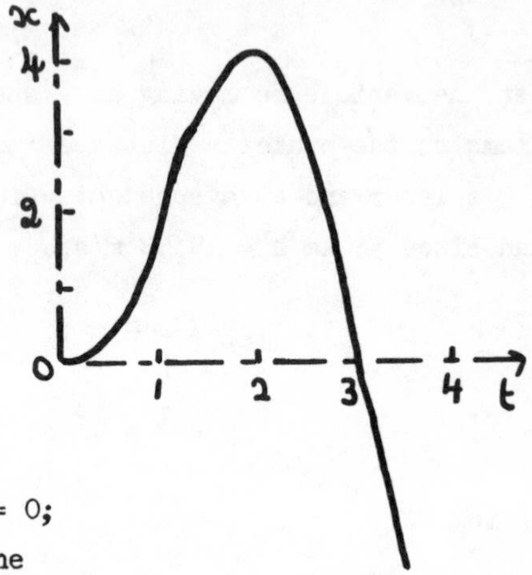

(a) at^2 must have dimensions of length L, so a must have dimensions of L/T^2; similarly, b of L/T^3 Ans.

(b) Using a = 3, b = 1 we have

$$x = 3t^2 - t^3,$$

which is shown plotted, with x in meters and t in seconds. Setting dx/dt = 0 gives $6t - 3t^2 = 0$; t = 0, 2. The value t = 2 gives the maximum x Ans.

(c) From t = 0 to t = 2 the particle travels x(2) - x(0) = 4 m. From t = 2 to t = 3 the particle travels $|x(3) - x(2)| = 4$ m. From t = 3 to t = 4 the particle travels $|x(4) - x(3)| = 16$ m. Thus the total distance travelled is 4 + 4 + 16 = 24 m Ans.

(d) Since x(4) = -16, the displacement is x(4) - x(0) = -16 m Ans.

(e) $v = dx/dt = 6t - 3t^2$. We get: (f) $a = dv/dt = 6(1 - t)$:

t	v(m/s)
1	3
2	0
3	-9
4	-24

t	a(m/s^2)
1	0
2	-6
3	-12
4	-18

(g) By definition,

$$v_{4,2} = \frac{x(4) - x(2)}{4 - 2} = -10 \text{ m/s Ans.}$$

3-31

Let the velocities of the ball striking and leaving the table be $\vec{v}_1$ and $\vec{v}_2$ respectively. Then, if the ball is in contact with the floor for a time T,

$$\bar{\vec{a}} = \frac{\vec{v}_2 - \vec{v}_1}{T}.$$

The directions of $\vec{v}_2$ and $\vec{v}_1$ are <u>up</u> and <u>down</u> respectively. Call the former direction -, the latter +, and we have

$$\bar{\vec{a}} = \frac{-v_2 + (-v_1)}{T} = -\frac{v_2 + v_1}{T}$$

so that $\bar{\vec{a}}$ is directed up.

Since the speed with which the ball leaves the ground is the same as the speed with which it would strike the ground if dropped from a height of 3.0 ft, v_1 and v_2 can both be found from

$$v^2 = 2\,g\,h,$$

using $h = 4$ ft for v_1, 3 ft for v_2; $g = 32\ \text{ft/s}^2$ in either case. Therefore $v_1 = 16$ ft/s and $v_2 = 13.86$ ft/s so that

$$\bar{\vec{a}} = \frac{13.86 + 16}{0.01} = 3000\ \text{ft/s}^2,\ \text{up}\ \underline{\text{Ans}}.$$

(This is about 93 g.)

<u>3-35</u>

Choose the positive x-axis vertical with origin at the ground. At $t = 0$ the package is released with velocity $\vec{v}_0$ directed upwards (i.e. $\vec{v}_0 = +12$ m/s) from height x_0. At $t = T$ it strikes the ground at $x = 0$. We have

$$x = \frac{1}{2}\,a\,t^2 + v_0 t + x_0.$$

Now $a = -9.8\ \text{m/s}^2$, since the acceleration is down, in the negative x-direction:

$$x = \frac{1}{2}(-9.8)t^2 + 12t + 80.$$

At $t = T$, $x = 0$:

$$0 = \frac{1}{2}(-9.8)T^2 + 12T + 80 \rightarrow T = 5.4\ \text{s}\ \underline{\text{Ans}}.$$

3-37

(a) The initial speed of the ball relative to the ground v is

$$v = 64 \text{ ft/s} + 32 \text{ ft/s} = 96 \text{ ft/s}.$$

If s is the height reached above the starting point,

$$v^2 = 2 g s,$$
$$(96)^2 = 2(32)s,$$
$$s = 144 \text{ ft}.$$

Since the starting point is 100 ft above ground, the highest point reached by the ball is 144 ft + 100 ft = 244 ft above ground Ans.

(b) Let t = time for the ball to reach maximum height. Then

$$v = g t \rightarrow t = 96/32 = 3 \text{ s}.$$

In this time the elevator has moved a distance $v_{el} t$ = (32 ft/s)(3 s) = 96 ft, so that the ball and elevator are separated by 144 - 96 = 48 ft at the moment when the ball is at its maximum height. Now let T = time for ball to fall to elevator floor from its maximum height. Then, relative to the elevator, the ball is projected downwards with a speed of v_{el} from a height of 48 ft. Choosing down as positive, origin at maximum height,

$$\frac{1}{2} g T^2 + v_{el} T + 0 = 48$$
$$\frac{1}{2}(32)T^2 + (32)T = 48$$
$$T = 1 \text{ s},$$

and therefore the total elapsed time is 3 s + 1 s = 4.0 s Ans.

3-42

Let y_1, y_2 be the distances of the first and second released bodies, respectively. Let the second body be released at t = 0. Then,

$$y_2 = \frac{1}{2} g t^2; \quad y_1 = \frac{1}{2} g (t + 1)^2.$$

We want $y_1 - y_2 = 10$ m; i.e.

$$\frac{1}{2} g (t + 1)^2 - \frac{1}{2} g t^2 = 10,$$

$$g(t + \frac{1}{2}) = 10.$$

Using $g = 9.8\ m/s^2$,

$$t = \frac{10}{9.8} - \frac{1}{2} = 0.52\ s.$$

Thus, the elapsed time since the first body was released is 0.52 s + 1 s = 1.52 s Ans.

3-45

Let the positive x-axis fixed on the elevator shaft be vertical, pointing upward, with x = 0 at that point of the shaft level with the elevator floor at the instant, t = 0, when the bolt left the elevator ceiling.

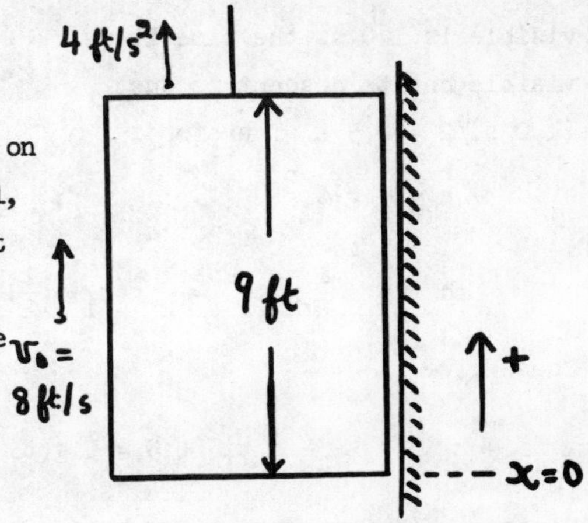

Also, let

x_b = position of bolt; x_f = position of elevator floor.

(a) Then, at any time,

$$x_b = \frac{1}{2}(-32)t^2 + 8\ t + 9; \quad x_f = \frac{1}{2}(4)t^2 + 8\ t.$$

If T = time of flight of the bolt, then when t = T, $x_b = x_f$:

$$-16\ T^2 + 8\ T + 9 = 2\ T^2 + 8\ T,$$

$$T^2 = \frac{1}{2} \rightarrow T = 0.71\ s\ \text{Ans.}$$

(b) Since the bolt started from the ceiling which is 9 ft above the floor, the desired distance is

$$D = 9 - x_f = 9 - 2\ T^2 - 8\ T = 9 - 1 - 5.68 \rightarrow D = 2.3\ \text{ft Ans.}$$

3-46

As indicated in the figure, let distances be measured from the highest point reached by the pot; also let the pot, in its descent, pass these various points at the times indicated.

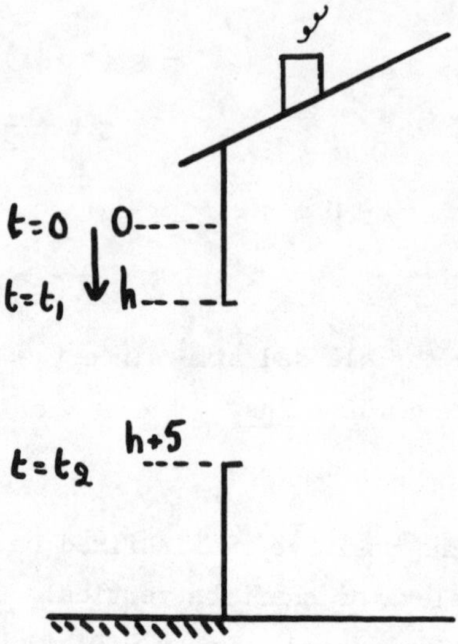

If the total time that the pot is visible is 1.0 s, the time it is visible on its descent is just (1.0 s)/2 = 0.5 s. Therefore,

$$h = \frac{1}{2} g t_1^2,$$

$$h + 5 = \frac{1}{2} g t_2^2 = \frac{1}{2} g(t_1 + \frac{1}{2})^2.$$

These give

$$\frac{1}{2} g t_1^2 + 5 = \frac{1}{2} g(t_1^2 + t_1 + \frac{1}{4});$$

Since $g = 32\ \text{ft/s}^2$ we get

$$t_1 = \frac{1}{16}\ \text{s},$$

yielding

$$h = \frac{1}{2}(32)(\frac{1}{16})^2 = \frac{1}{16}\ \text{ft}\ \underline{\text{Ans}}.$$

CHAPTER 4

4-2

$$\vec{r}(t) = \vec{i} + 4t^2\,\vec{j} + t\,\vec{k}.$$

By definition of velocity and acceleration,

(a) $\vec{v} = d\vec{r}/dt = 8t\,\vec{j} + \vec{k}$ Ans., $\vec{a} = d\vec{v}/dt = 8\,\vec{j}$ Ans.

(b) Since $\vec{a}$ is independent of the time t, the acceleration is constant and the path is a parabola. The x-coordinate does not vary with time, so the motion is in the y, z-plane cutting the x-axis at x = 1.

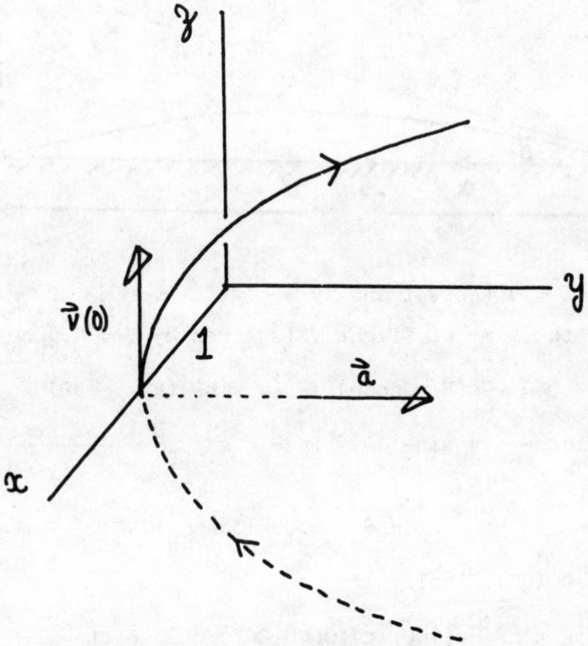

4-4

(a) The acceleration in the horizontal direction is zero; therefore the horizontal component of the velocity is unchanged during the motion. Since this is $v_0\cos\theta_0$ at launching, it is $v_0\cos\theta_0$ in the same direction at the top of the trajectory. But the vertical velocity is zero at the top of the path, so the speed of the particle at the top is just $v_0\cos\theta_0$ (the direction of the velocity there is, of course, horizontal).

(b) The acceleration is due to the gravity field of the earth which persists (we hope) throughout the motion. Thus, the acceleration is g, vertically down.

(c) From (a) and (b), they are perpendicular.

4-6

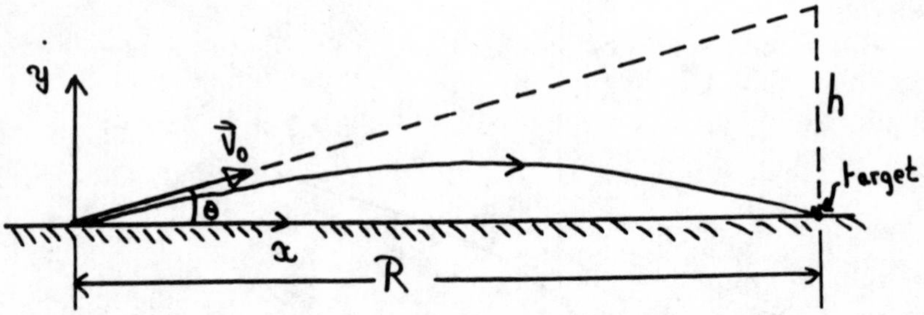

We have that $x = v_0(\cos\theta)t$ and $y = -\frac{1}{2}gt^2 + v_0\sin\theta\ t$. When $x = R$, $y = 0$ so that the time of flight T is given by $T = R/v_0\cos\theta$. Thus,

$$0 = -\frac{1}{2}g(R/v_0\cos\theta)^2 + (v_0\sin\theta)(R/v_0\cos\theta)$$

$$0 = -\frac{1}{2}gR/v_0\cos\theta + v_0\sin\theta \quad \rightarrow \quad \sin2\theta = gR/v_0{}^2 = \frac{(32\ \text{ft/s}^2)(150\ \text{ft})}{(1500\ \text{ft/s})^2}$$

$$\sin2\theta = 0.002133 \ll 1,$$

so that $\theta = 0.001067$. Finally,

$$h = R\tan\theta = (150\ \text{ft})(0.001067) = 0.16\ \text{ft} = 1.9\ \text{in}\ \underline{\text{Ans.}}$$

4-11

We use $\sin53° = 4/5$, $\cos53° = 3/5$ and orient the coordinate system as shown. The bomb is released at $t = 0$ and its time of flight is T, so that when $t = T$, $y = 0$. Thus $y_0 = +730$ m and $v_{y0} = -v\cos53°$ and we have

(a) $$0 = -\frac{1}{2}gT^2 - (v\cos 53^\circ)T + 730 \rightarrow v = 202 \text{ m/s } \underline{\text{Ans.}},$$

since $T = 5.0$ s and $g = 9.8$ m/s^2.

(b) The horizontal velocity remains unchanged so,

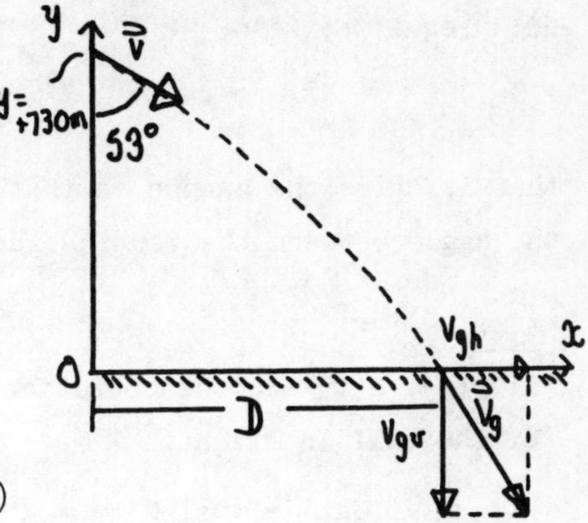

$$D = (v\sin 53^\circ)T$$

$$= (202 \text{ m/s})(4/5)(5 \text{ s})$$

$$= 808 \text{ m } \underline{\text{Ans.}}$$

(c) As the bomb impacts,

$$v_{gh} = v_x = (202 \text{ m/s})(4/5)$$

$$= 162 \text{ m/s } \underline{\text{Ans.}}$$

$$v_{gv} = (v\cos 53^\circ) + gT$$

$$= (202 \text{ m/s})(3/5) + (9.8 \text{ m/s}^2)(5 \text{ s})$$

$$= 170 \text{ m/s } \underline{\text{Ans.}}$$

4-19

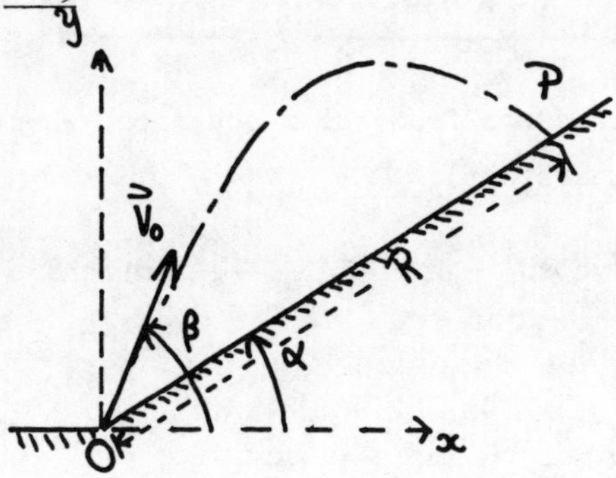

If g = magnitude of acceleration due to gravity, it is apparent that

$$y = -\frac{1}{2}gt^2 + (v_0\sin\beta)t,$$
$$x = (v_0\cos\beta)t,$$

where x and y are the coordinates of the shell. The coordinates of the impact point are

$$x_P = R\cos\alpha, \quad y_P = R\sin\alpha.$$

Hence, if T is the time of flight,

$$R\cos\alpha = (v_0\cos\beta)T \rightarrow T = R\cos\alpha/v_0\cos\beta.$$

Therefore,

$$y_P = R\sin\alpha = -\frac{1}{2}g(R\cos\alpha/v_0\cos\beta)^2 + (v_0\sin\beta)(R\cos\alpha)/v_0\cos\beta);$$

Solving for R gives

$$R = \frac{2v_0^2}{g\cos^2\alpha}\cos\beta\,\sin(\beta - \alpha).$$

To find the maximum range with variations in elevation angle β, set $dR/d\beta$ equal to zero:

$$\frac{dR}{d\beta} = 0 \rightarrow \beta = \frac{\pi}{4} + \frac{\alpha}{2} \quad \underline{\text{Ans.}};$$

that is, fire the cannon so that the shell's initial velocity bisects the angle between the vertical and the slope of the hill.

4-20

If $y(t)$, $x(t)$ are the coordinates of the ball in flight,

$$y = -\tfrac{1}{2}gt^2 + (v\sin\beta)t,$$
$$x = (v\cos\beta)t.$$

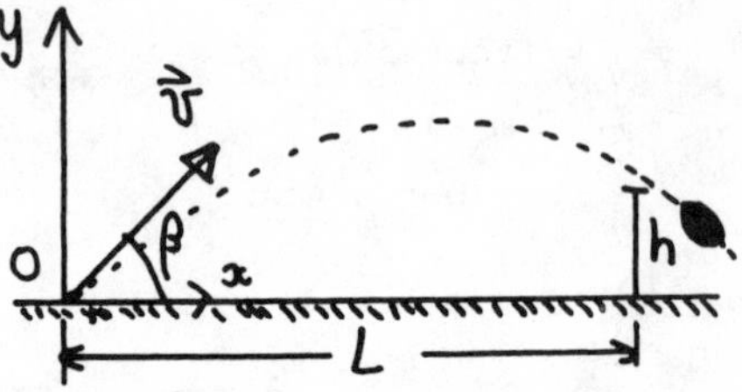

Let T = time from kick to the instant when the ball reaches a horizontal distance L; then $T = L/v\cos\beta$, from the x-equation. When $t = T$ we want $y = h$ (ball just clears bar):

$$h = -\tfrac{1}{2}g(L/v\cos\beta)^2 + (v\sin\beta)(L/v\cos\beta) \rightarrow h = -\tfrac{1}{2}g\frac{L^2}{v^2\cos^2\beta} + L\tan\beta.$$

If we let

$$a = \tfrac{1}{2}g\frac{L^2}{v^2} = \tfrac{1}{2}g\frac{(50\text{ m})^2}{(25\text{ m/s})^2} = 19.60\text{ m};\ x = \tan\beta,$$

the equation for h will become

$$ax^2 - Lx + (h + a) = 0 \rightarrow 19.60\,x^2 - 50\,x + 23.04 = 0,$$

since $h = 3.44$ m and $L = 50$ m. Solving for the two values of x gives $\beta = 31°, 63°$ for the limits <u>Ans.</u>

4-27

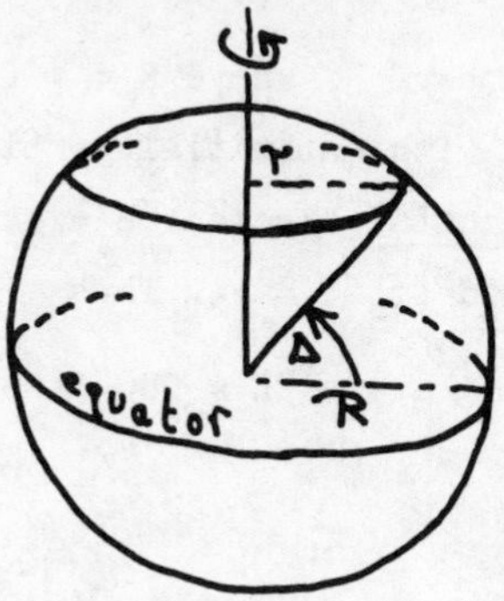

Let R = radius of the earth and Δ = latitude of the object; also T = period of the earth's rotation Then

$$vT = 2\pi r,$$

where v is the speed of the object due to rotation and $r = R\cos\Delta$.

The acceleration is

$$a = \frac{v^2}{r} = \frac{4\pi^2 r^2/T^2}{r} = 4\pi^2 \frac{r}{T^2}$$

$$= 4\pi^2 \frac{R\cos\Delta}{T^2}.$$

The numerical values required here are

$$R = 6.378 \times 10^6 \text{ m}; \; T = 23 \text{ h } 56 \text{ min} = 86,160 \text{ s}.$$

Thus we have at

(a) the equator, $\Delta = 0$, $a = 3.4 \times 10^{-2}$ m/s^2 Ans.,

(b) latitude 60°, $\Delta = 60°$, $\cos\Delta = 1/2$, $a = 1.7 \times 10^{-2}$ m/s^2 Ans.

(c) If T' = the rotation period of the earth if the acceleration at the equator = g, then ($\Delta = 0$)

$$g = 4\pi^2 R/T'^2.$$

In reality

$$a = 4\pi^2 R/T^2.$$

Therefore,

$$a/g = 3.397 \times 10^{-2}/9.8 = T'^2/T^2 \rightarrow T' = 0.0589T \cong T/17,$$

which means that the earth would have to be spinning 17 times faster than it is Ans.

4-28

The acceleration in circular motion is $a = v^2/R$, where R = 4 ft. We need v. But, since the object falls 6 ft with an initial vertical speed of zero (stone was swung in a horizontal circle), $6 = gt^2/2$. Also, the horizontal velocity is conserved so 30 = vt. Thus

$$6 = \frac{1}{2}g\frac{900}{v^2} \rightarrow v^2 = \frac{1}{2}g\frac{900}{6} \rightarrow a = v^2/R = 600\ \text{ft/s}^2\ \text{Ans.}$$

since $g = 32\ \text{ft/s}^2$ and R = 4 ft.

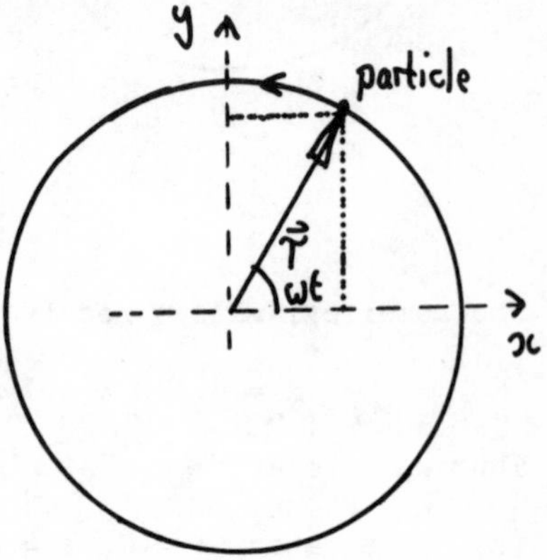

4-30

(a) From the figure, $\omega = v/r$,

$\vec{r} = r\cos\omega t\ \vec{i} + r\sin\omega t\ \vec{j}$ Ans.

(b) Since $\vec{v} = d\vec{r}/dt$,

$\vec{v} = -r\omega\sin\omega t\ \vec{i} + r\omega\cos\omega t\ \vec{j}$ Ans.

and $\vec{a} = d\vec{v}/dt$ so that

$\vec{a} = -r\omega^2\cos\omega t\ \vec{i} - r\omega^2\sin\omega t\ \vec{j}$ Ans.

(c) From (a) and (b) we see that $\vec{a} = -\omega^2\vec{r}$; since ω^2 is a scalar > 0, $\vec{a}$ is antiparallel to $\vec{r}$ and therefore points to the center of the circle.

4-35

Let

$\vec{v}_{rt}$ = velocity of rain relative to train,
$\vec{v}_{rg}$ = velocity of rain relative to ground,
$\vec{v}_{tg}$ = velocity of train relative to ground.

Then we have

$$\vec{v}_{rt} + \vec{v}_{tg} = \vec{v}_{rg},$$

and this is illustrated in the figure.

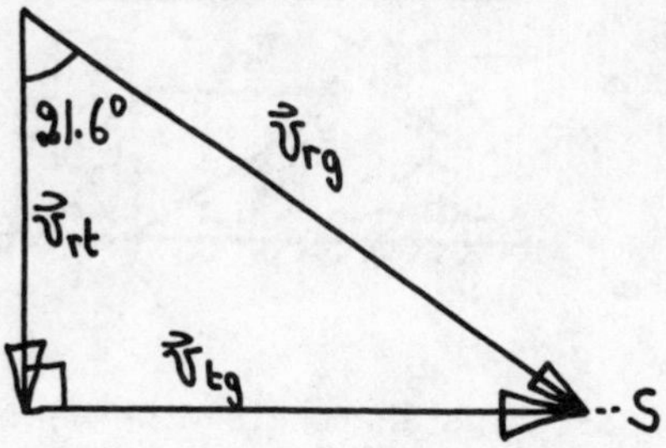

Since $v_{tg} = 88.2$ ft/s,

$$v_{rg} = \frac{v_{tg}}{\sin 21.6°} = \frac{88.2 \text{ ft/s}}{0.36812}$$

$$v_{rg} = 240 \text{ ft/s } \underline{\text{Ans.}}$$

4-38

If

$\vec{v}_{rg}$ = velocity of river relative to ground (parallel to banks of river),

$\vec{v}_{br}$ = velocity of boat relative to river (v_{br} = 4 mi/h),

$\vec{v}_{bg}$ = velocity of boat relative to ground,

then

$$\vec{v}_{br} + \vec{v}_{rg} = \vec{v}_{bg}.$$

(a) Here we want $\vec{v}_{bg}$ headed perpendicular to the river banks.

$$\sin\alpha = \frac{v_{rg}}{v_{br}} = \frac{2 \text{ mi/h}}{4 \text{ mi/h}} \rightarrow \alpha = 30°;$$

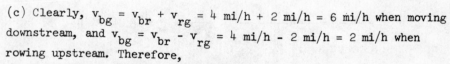

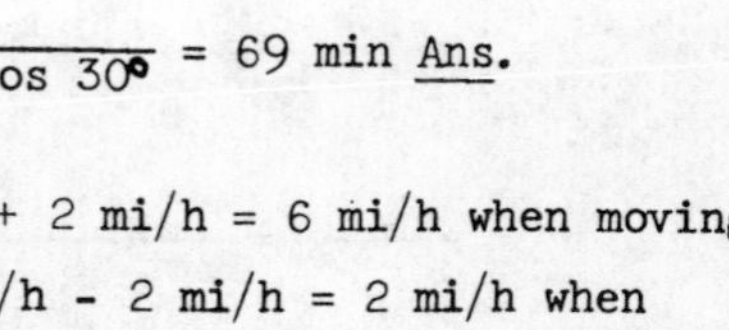

that is, he should head the boat 30° upstream Ans.

(b) If T is the crossing time,

$$T = \frac{D}{v_{bg}} = \frac{D}{v_{br}\cos\alpha} = \frac{4 \text{ mi}}{(4 \text{ mi/h})\cos 30°} = 69 \text{ min } \underline{\text{Ans.}}$$

(c) Clearly, $v_{bg} = v_{br} + v_{rg}$ = 4 mi/h + 2 mi/h = 6 mi/h when moving downstream, and $v_{bg} = v_{br} - v_{rg}$ = 4 mi/h - 2 mi/h = 2 mi/h when rowing upstream. Therefore,

$$T = \frac{2 \text{ mi}}{6 \text{ mi/h}} + \frac{2 \text{ mi}}{2 \text{ mi/h}} = 1\tfrac{1}{3} \text{ h} = 80 \text{ min } \underline{\text{Ans.}}$$

(d) Since this is just (c) in reverse, T = 80 min also Ans.

(e) To cross in the shortest time we want $\vec{v}_{bg}$ to have as large a component perpendicular to the banks as possible. Now $\vec{v}_{bg} = \vec{v}_{br} + \vec{v}_{rg}$, but $\vec{v}_{rg}$ is directed parallel to the banks, and so cannot affect the velocity of the boat perpendicular to the banks. Thus, to make this last as large as possible we head the boat directly across the river. Then

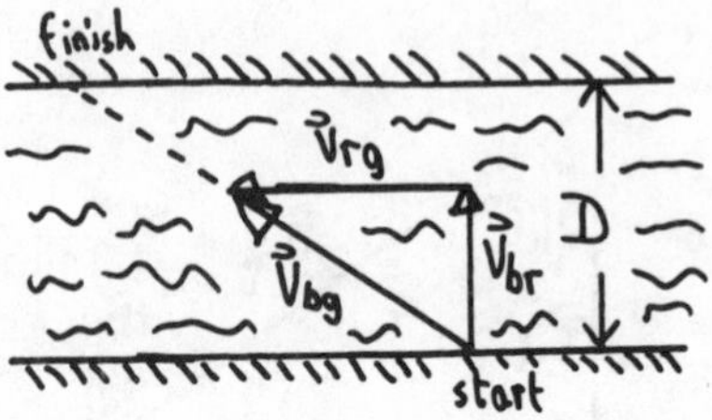

$$T = \frac{D}{v_{br}} = \frac{4\ \text{mi}}{4\ \text{mi/h}} = 1\ \text{h} = 60\ \text{min}\ \underline{\text{Ans.}}$$

Of course, the boat ends up somewhere downstream.

4-41

Let t = time required to get up the escalator, and

w = person's walking speed,

s = escalator speed,

m = person's speed when walking on escalator (relative to ground),

L = length of escalator.

Then,

$$L/w = t_w = 90\ \text{s};\ L/s = t_s = 60\ \text{s};\ L/m = t_m$$

where t_m is the time to walk up the moving escalator. Clearly,

$$m = s + w,$$

so that

$$t_m = \frac{L}{s + w} = \frac{L}{L/t_s + L/t_w} = \frac{1}{1/60 + 1/90} = 36\ \text{s}\ \underline{\text{Ans.}}$$

CHAPTER 5

5-3

Draw free-body diagrams for the blocks, and apply Newton's second law to the horizontal forces. Assuming that the blocks move together so that their accelerations are the same (the force of contact F_c would be zero otherwise) we get

(a)

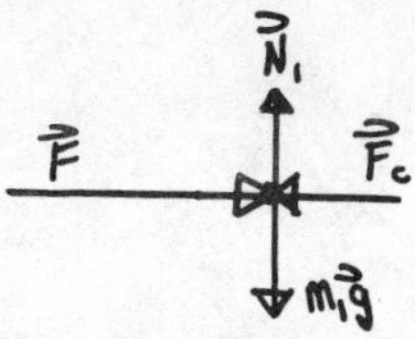

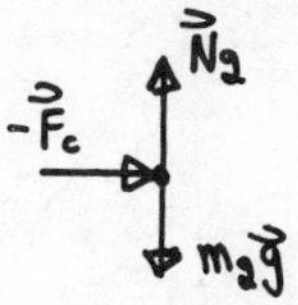

$$F - F_c = m_1 a, \qquad F_c = m_2 a.$$

Eliminating the acceleration gives

$$F_c = \frac{m_2}{m_1 + m_2} F = \frac{1}{2 + 1}(3.0 \text{ N}) = 1.0 \text{ N} \; \underline{\text{Ans.}}$$

(b) Here it is only necessary to interchange the blocks:

$$F_c = \frac{m_1}{m_2 + m_1} F = \frac{2}{1 + 2}(3.0 \text{ N}) = 2.0 \text{ N} \; \underline{\text{Ans.}}$$

The acceleration is the same in parts (a) and (b). On one of the blocks, the force of contact F_c is the force that provides this acceleration and, by Newton's second law, this force is proportional to the mass.

5-10

By definition, the average acceleration is

(a) $$\bar{a} = \frac{v_f - v_i}{t_f - t_i},$$

where v_i, v_f are the initial and final velocitites with which the man strikes the patio (at times t_i and t_f). Now $v_f = 0$, and if he jumps from height h,

$$v_i = \sqrt{2gh} = \sqrt{2(9.8\ m/s^2)(0.5\ m)} = 3.13\ m/s.$$

The motion is arrested in a distance d, and with $\bar{v}$ the average speed during this time

$$\bar{v}(t_f - t_i) = d.$$

A good approximation is to let $\bar{v} = \frac{1}{2}v_i$, since $v_f = 0$. This gives

$$t_f - t_i = \frac{0.02\ m}{\frac{1}{2}(3.13\ m/s)} = 0.0128\ s,$$

and therefore

$$\bar{a} = \frac{3.13\ m/s}{0.0128\ s} = 245\ m/s^2, \text{ upward } \underline{\text{Ans.}}$$

(b) The average force is

$$\bar{F} = (80\ kg)(245\ m/s^2) = 2.0 \times 10^4\ N\ \underline{\text{Ans.}}$$

5-12

With Newton's second law applied to the body, one observes that

$$mg - F_r = + ma$$

$$F_r = m(g - a)$$

$$F_r = (0.25\ kg)(9.8 - 9.2)m/s^2$$

$$F_r = 0.15\ N\ \underline{\text{Ans.}}$$

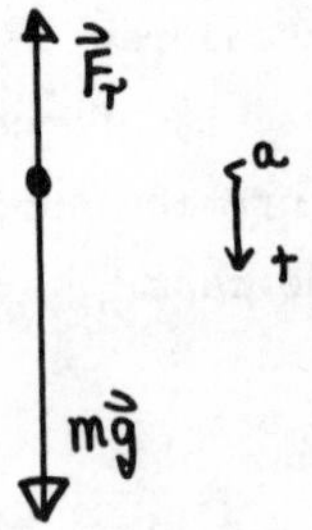

5-14

(a) Look at the forces acting on an element of mass δm of the rope: the weight of this element must be balanced by upward vertical components of the tension. Since the tension is directed along the rope, it must sag.

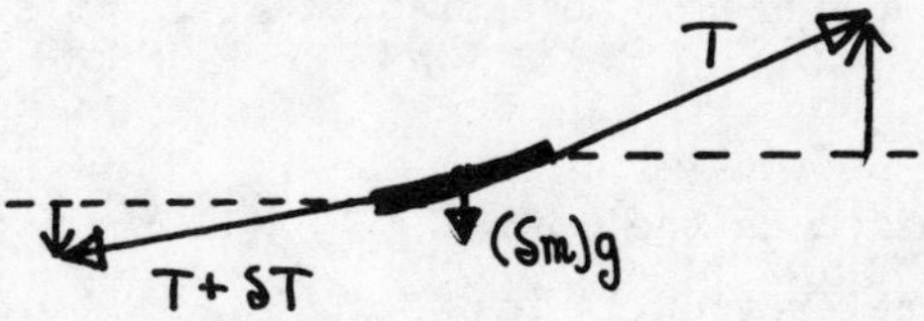

(b) For the rope and the block, the equations of motion are

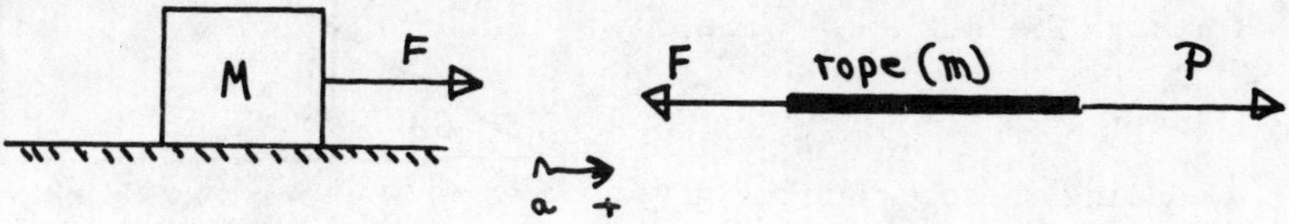

$$F = Ma, \qquad P - F = ma,$$

where F is the force the rope exerts on the block. Adding these equations,

$$P = (m + M)a \rightarrow a = \frac{P}{m + M} \quad \underline{\text{Ans.}}$$

(c) Directly from (b),

$$F = Ma = \frac{M}{m + M} P \quad \underline{\text{Ans.}}$$

(d) Draw a free-body diagram for the leading half of the rope.

$$P - T = \frac{m}{2} a = \frac{m}{2} \frac{P}{m + M} \rightarrow T = \frac{P}{2} \frac{m + 2M}{m + M} \quad \underline{\text{Ans.}}$$

5-17

The feature to note is that the tension in the cord can be less than the weight of the block if the block is accelerated.

$$W - T = + ma \rightarrow T = W(1 - \frac{a}{g}).$$

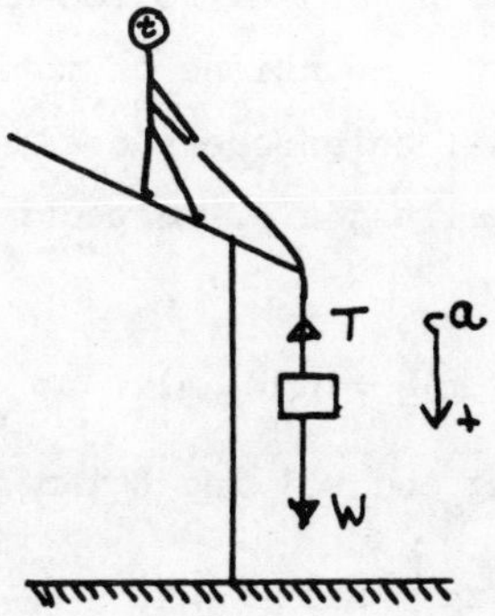

With W = 100 lb, T = 87 lb, one gets $a = 4.2 \text{ ft/s}^2$. Thus, lower the object with a downward acceleration $\geqslant 4.2\ \text{ft/s}^2$ Ans.

5-19

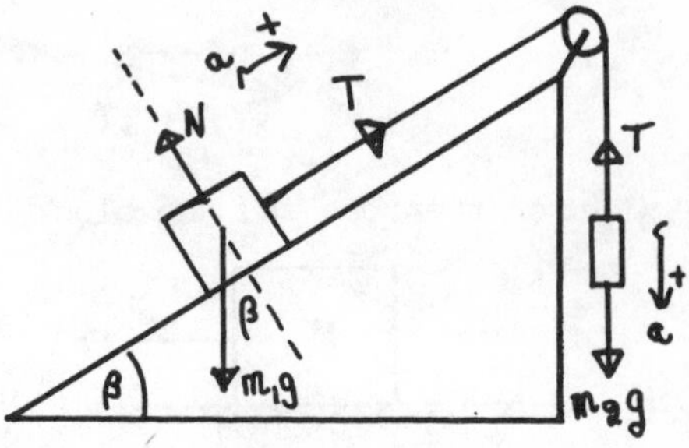

Let T be the tension in the cord; we assume the acceleration is in the direction shown. Then,

for m_1: $T - m_1 g \sin\beta = m_1 a$;

for m_2: $m_2 g - T = m_2 a$.

(a) Adding these equations gives

$$a = \frac{m_2 - m_1 \sin\beta}{m_1 + m_2}\, g = \frac{2.0 - 3.0 \sin\pi/6}{2.0 + 3.0}\, g = g/10 = 3.2\ \text{ft/s}^2.$$

Since $a > 0$, the direction of the acceleration that was assumed above was correct Ans.

(b) From the equation for m_2,

$$T = m_2(g - a) = (2.0\ \text{slug})(32 - 3.2)\ \text{ft/s}^2$$

$$T = 58\ \text{lb}$$ Ans.

5-24

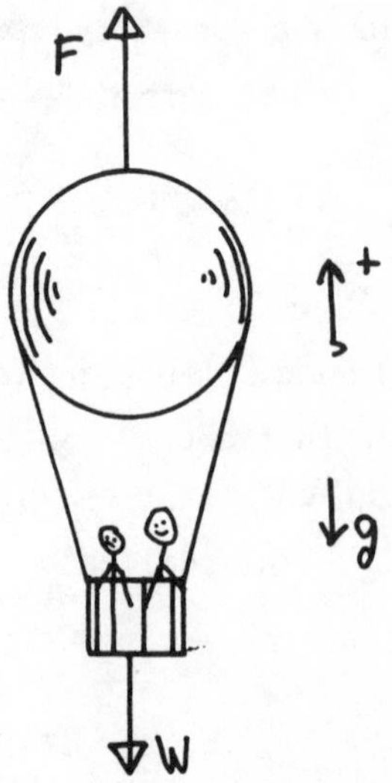

Let F be the upward lift of the balloon (assumed constant) and m the mass of ballast discarded. If we take the upward direction as positive, the equations of motion for the balloon before and after dropping ballast are, respectivelly,

$$F - Mg = -Ma,$$

$$F - (M - m)g = (M - m)a.$$

Subtracting and solving for m gives

$$m = 2M \frac{a}{a + g}$$ Ans.

5-25

Draw free-body diagrams of the cage, counterweight and mechanism, and apply Newton's second law to each.

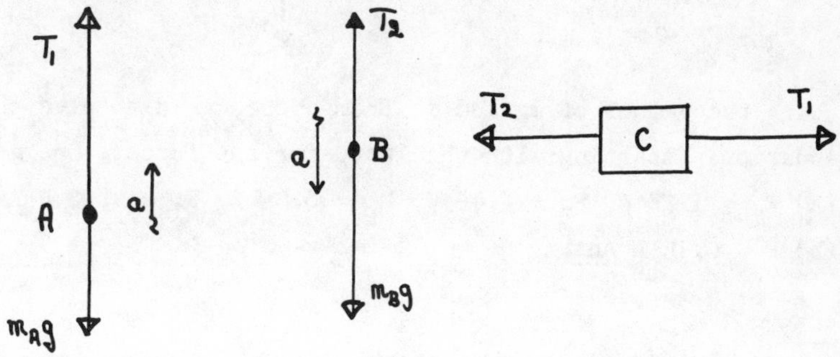

(a) $T_1 - m_A g = m_A a$, (b) $m_B g - T_2 = m_B a$,

$T_1 = m_A(g + a) = (1100)(9.8 + 2)$, $T_2 = m_B(g - a) = (1000)(9.8 - 2)$,

$T_1 = 13{,}000$ N Ans. $T_2 = 7800$ N Ans.

(c) The net force $\vec{F} = \vec{T}_1 + \vec{T}_2$ exerted by the cable on the mechanism is just $F = T_1 - T_2 = 13{,}000 - 7800 = 5200$ N, to the right. Hence, by Newton's third law, the force exerted on the cable by the mechanism is 5200 N, to the left, given the arrangement above Ans.

5-32

To apply Newton's second law to each link, each of mass m, we need the quantities,

$mg = (0.10\ \text{kg})(9.8\ \text{m/s}^2) = 0.98$ N, $ma = (0.10)(2.5)$ N $= 0.25$ N.

Hence we have immediately, from the latter, that (c) the net force on any link = ma = 0.25 N, upwards Ans. Now let F_i = forces between links and F be the external force lifting the chain. Then we have,

1 st link:

$F - F_1 - mg = ma.$

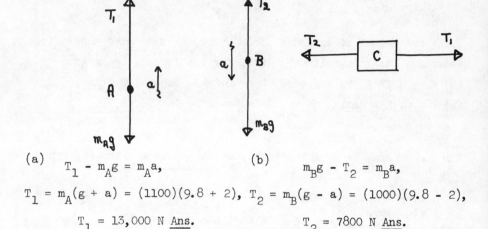

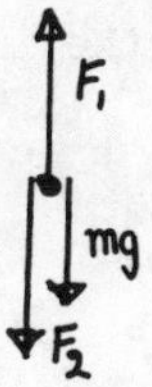

2 nd link:

$F_1 - F_2 - mg = ma.$

Similarly for the next two links giving,

$$F_2 - F_3 - mg = ma,$$

$$F_3 - F_4 - mg = ma.$$

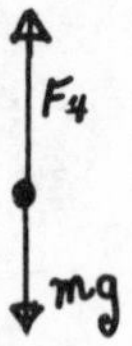

Last link:

$$F_4 - mg = ma.$$

Using the values of mg and ma from above, we can solve these five equations, starting with the last, for the forces. One gets:

(a) $F_4 = 1.23$ N, $F_3 = 2.46$ N, $F_2 = 3.69$ N, $F_1 = 4.92$ N Ans;

(b) $F = 6.15$ N Ans.

5-35

The x,y- frame is attached to the earth and is an inertial frame.

Let

$\vec{a}'$ = acceleration of block wrt elevator,

$\vec{a}''$ = acceleration of block wrt earth,

$\vec{a}$ = acceleration of elevator wrt earth.

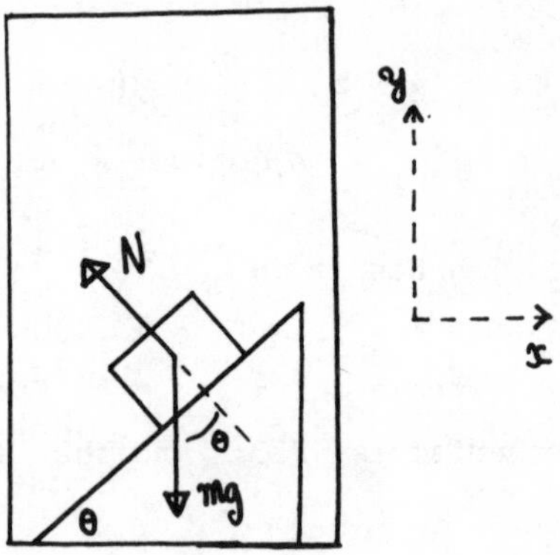

(a),(b) In these cases a = 0, and the elevator is also an inertial frame, so we have

$\vec{a}' = g \sin\theta$, down the incline Ans.

(c) The elevator is no longer an inertial frame, so we must apply Newton's second law in the x,y-frame:

$$N \cos\theta - mg = ma''_y, \qquad - N \sin\theta = ma''_x.$$

But

$$\vec{a}' + \vec{a} = \vec{a}''.$$

Clearly, $\vec{a}'$ is parallel to the incline, so that

$$\vec{a}' = - a' \cos\theta \,\vec{i} - a' \sin\theta \,\vec{j}.$$

Then, since $\vec{a} = - a\vec{j}$, we have

$$\vec{a}'' = - a' \cos\theta \,\vec{i} - (a + a' \sin\theta)\,\vec{j}.$$

Substitute this into Newton's second law, above, and obtain

$N \cos\theta - mg = - m(a + a' \sin\theta), \qquad - N \sin\theta = - m\, a' \cos\theta.$

These equations may be solved for a' by eliminating N:

$$a' = (g - a)\sin\theta, \text{ down the incline } \underline{\text{Ans}}.$$

(d) Here the analysis is the same as in (c), except that a is replaced with -a, giving

$$a' = (g + a)\sin\theta, \text{ down the incline, } \underline{\text{Ans}}.$$

(e) In this case, we use the result from (c), but putting $a = g$. The result is $a' = 0$ Ans.

(f) Again, use the equations in part (c), only this time eliminate a' and solve for N:

$$N = m(g - a)\cos\theta \ \underline{\text{Ans}}$$

is the result.

CHAPTER 6

6-1

(a) Let v be the initial speed, s the distance required to come to a stop. The only force acting in the horizontal direction is the force of friction F_k. Therefore,

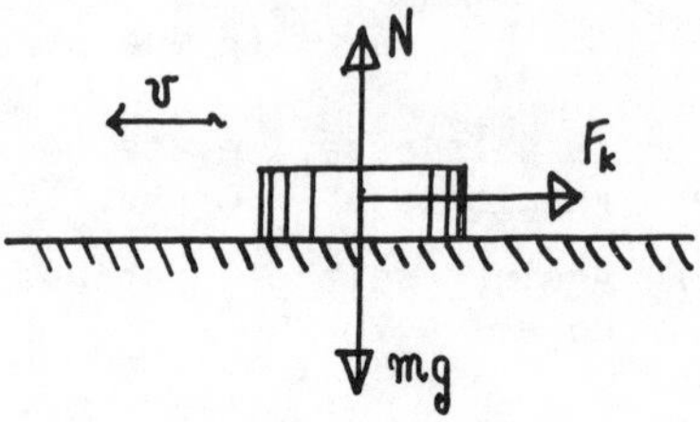

$$F_k = m\ a.$$

But $v^2 = 2\ a\ s$ giving

$$(20\ ft/s)^2 = 2\ a\ (50\ ft) \rightarrow a = 4\ ft/s^2.$$

Thus

$$F_k = \frac{0.25\ lb}{32\ ft/s^2}(4\ ft/s^2) = 0.031\ lb\ \underline{Ans.}$$

(b) Since the force of friction is $\mu_k N$ and $N = mg$ in this case,

$$F_k = ma = \mu_k mg \rightarrow \mu_k = \frac{a}{g} = 4/32 = 0.125\ \underline{Ans.}$$

6-5

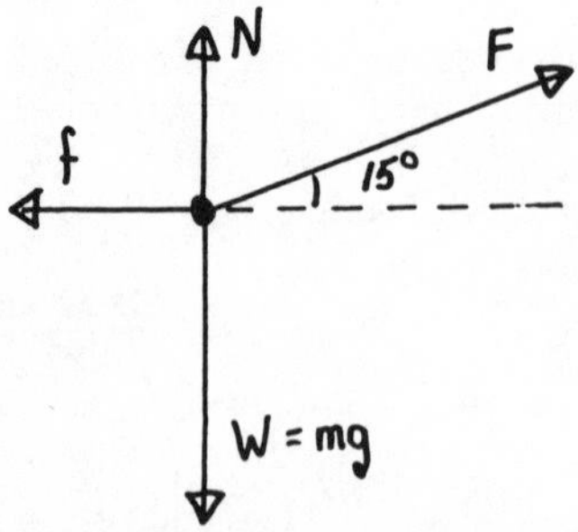

The man pulls with a force F, and the force of friction is f.

(a) With the crate on the verge of moving, $f = \mu_s N$. Note that $N \neq mg$ in this case since part of the weight is balanced by the vertical component of F. Applying Newton's second law gives

$$F\cos 15° - \mu_s N = 0,$$

$$N + F\sin 15° - W = 0.$$

We may eliminate N between these equations and solve for F:

$$F = \frac{\mu_s W}{\cos 15° + \mu_s \sin 15°} = \frac{(0.5)(150\text{ lb})}{(0.96593) + (0.5)(0.25882)} = 68.47\text{ lb},$$

or to two significant figures, F = 68 lb Ans.

(b) With the crate moving, $f = \mu_k N$. The equations of motion are

$$F\cos 15° - \mu_k N = ma = \frac{W}{g}a, \qquad N + F\sin 15° - W = 0.$$

These give for the acceleration,

$$a = g\left[\frac{F}{W}(\cos 15° + \mu_k \sin 15°) - \mu_k\right] = 4.2\text{ ft/s}^2 \text{ Ans},$$

after substituting numerical values.

6-11

(a) Clearly, if the block slips, it will slip downward; hence the force of static friction $\vec{f}$ points upward. The block will not move horizontally, so that N = F = 12 lb. The maximum available force of friction is $\mu_s N$ = (0.6)(12 lb) = 7.2 lb. Since this is greater than the weight of the block (5 lb), the block will not move.

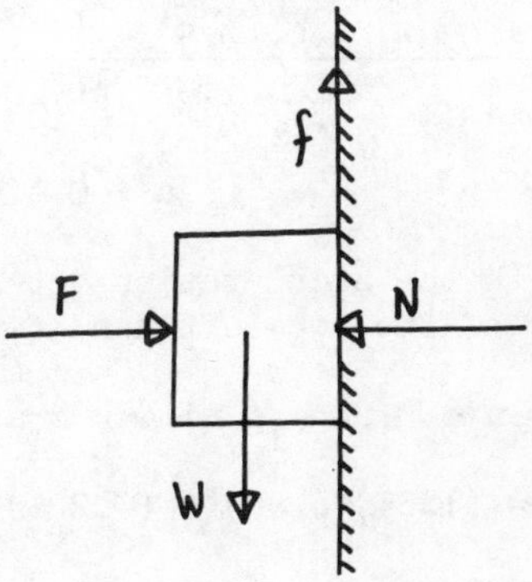

(b) The force of friction will be no greater than the weight of the block, for if it were, the block would accelerate up the wall.
We conclude that the forces exerted by the wall on the block are a force N = 12 lb to the left, and a force f of friction equal to 5 lb directed upward.

6-14

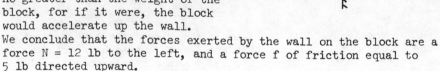

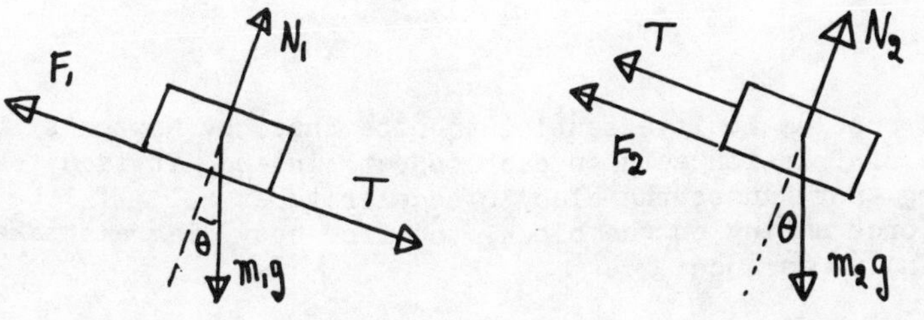

The force diagrams are as shown on the previous page, with the forces of friction given by $F_1 = \mu_1 N_1$ and $F_2 = \mu_2 N_2$. Taking components parallel and perpendicular to the plane:

$$T + m_1 g \sin\theta - F_1 = m_1 a, \qquad N_1 - m_1 g \cos\theta = 0;$$
$$m_2 g \sin\theta - T - F_2 = m_2 a, \qquad N_2 - m_2 g \cos\theta = 0.$$

(b) Add the two left-hand equations and put in the values of F_1 and F_2 using the right-hand equations to obtain

$$m_1 g \sin\theta - F_1 + m_2 g \sin\theta - F_2 = (m_1 + m_2)a,$$

or,

$$a = \frac{(m_1 + m_2)\sin\theta - (\mu_1 m_1 + \mu_2 m_2)\cos\theta}{(m_1 + m_2)} g$$

$$= \frac{(1.65 + 3.30)(0.5) - [(0.226)(1.65) + (0.113)(3.30)](0.866)}{(1.65 + 3.30)} g,$$

$$a = 0.370\ g = 3.62\ \mathrm{m/s^2}$$ Ans.

(a) With the acceleration determined, we can find the tension from either of the two left-hand force equations: e.g. from the first,

$$T = m_1 a + F_1 - m_1 g \sin\theta = m_1 a + \mu_1 m_1 g \cos\theta - m_1 g \sin\theta$$

$$= (1.65)(3.62) + (0.226)(1.65)(9.8)(0.866) - (1.65)(9.8)(0.5),$$

$$T = 1.05\ \mathrm{N}$$ Ans.

(c) The acceleration is the same if the blocks are reversed, since the 'object' sliding is unchanged. Hence T would have the same magnitude and direction as applied to each body separately; i.e. T applied to mass 1 would still be down the plane. If this mass is leading, the rod will be under compression and not tension as above.

6-17

In this problem it is essential to note that, by Newton's third law, a force of friction acts on each object; indeed, it is a force of friction that causes the slab to accelerate at all. If F be the 100 N force acting on the block, the free-body diagrams take on the following appearance:

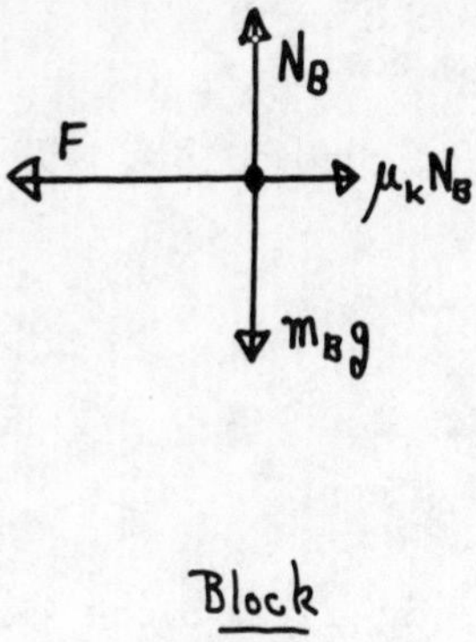

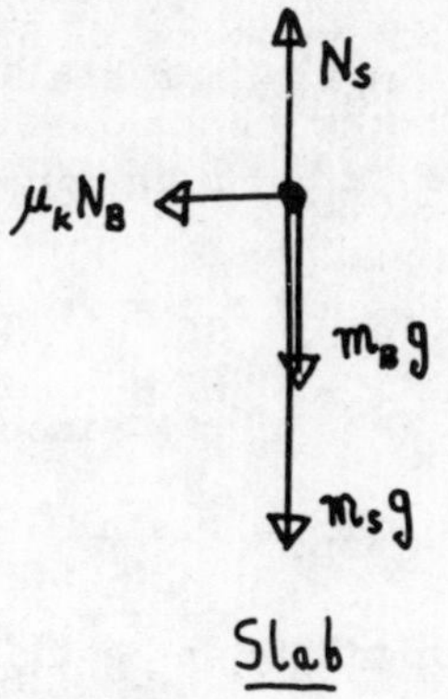

The equations of motion follow directly from the free-body diagrams.

(a) For the block, since $N_B = m_B g$,

$$F - \mu_k m_B g = m_B a,$$

$$100\text{ N} - (0.4)(10\text{ kg})(9.8\text{ m/s}^2) = (10\text{ kg})\,a,$$

$$a = 6.1\text{ m/s}^2 \quad \underline{\text{Ans.}}$$

(b) For the slab, of which the acceleration is a',

$$\mu_k N_B = m_s a',$$

$$\mu_k m_B g = m_s a',$$

$$a' = \mu_k (m_B/m_s) g = (0.4)(10/40)(9.8\text{ m/s}^2),$$

$$a' = 0.98\text{ m/s}^2 \quad \underline{\text{Ans.}}$$

6-19

We show the force diagram with the 8-lb block leading.

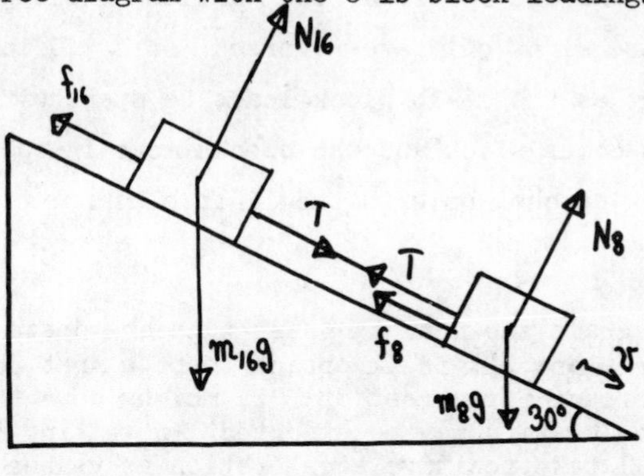

(a) Since

$$f_{16} = \mu_{16} m_{16} g \cos 30°, \qquad f_8 = \mu_8 m_8 g \cos 30°,$$

we have,

$$m_8a_8 = m_8g \sin 30° - T - \mu_8 m_8 g \cos 30°,$$

$$m_{16}a_{16} = m_{16}g \sin 30° + T - \mu_{16} m_{16} g \cos 30°.$$

Now $\mu_{16} = 2\mu_8$ and $m_{16} = 2m_8$. Therefore

$$a_8 = g \sin 30° - T/m_8 - \mu_8 g \cos 30°,$$

$$a_{16} = g \sin 30° + T/m_{16} - 2\mu_8 g \cos 30°.$$

If T = 0 initially, $a_8 > a_{16}$. Therefore, the first block will eventually pull on the second, and subsequently there will be a tension in the string. The blocks move together with a common acceleration a. Setting $a_8 = a_{16} = a$ in the equations of motion and adding them gives,

$$(m_8 + m_{16})a = (m_8 + m_{16})\, g \sin 30° - g \cos 30° (m_8\mu_8 + m_{16}\mu_{16}),$$

$$a = 11.38 \rightarrow 11 \text{ ft/s}^2 \quad \underline{\text{Ans.}}$$

(b) Clearly,

$$T = m_{16}a - m_{16}g \sin 30° + \mu_{16} m_{16} g \cos 30° = 0.46 \text{ lb} \quad \underline{\text{Ans.}}$$

(c) If the blocks are reversed, the same equations of motion hold, except that the signs of T are reversed. If T = 0 initially, $a_8 > a_{16}$ as before. But as the 16-lb block leads to start with, the string immediately becomes slack and the blocks move independently, unless the 8-lb block catches up with the 16-lb block.

6-20

The force diagrams shown on the next page are drawn for block B moving up the plane. It is important to note that the direction of the friction force $\vec{f}$ reverses if B is moving down the plane, and a different acceleration may be expected. In writing the equations of motion we will take positive acceleration as up the plane; -f then corresponds to B moving up the plane, +f to B moving down. Notice that there is no obvious correlation between the directions of the acceleration and velocity of the blocks.

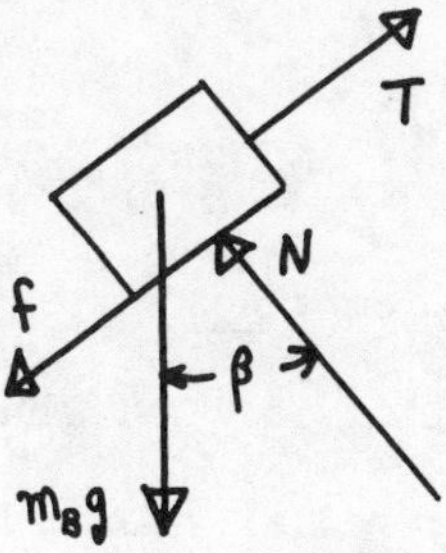

The equations of motion are:

$$m_A g - T = m_A a, \quad (1) \qquad T \mp f - m_B g \sin\beta = m_B a, \quad (2)$$

$$f = \mu N, \quad (3) \qquad N - m_B g \cos\beta = 0. \quad (4)$$

Adding (1) and (2), and substituting the value of f from (3) and (4), gives for the acceleration,

$$a = \frac{m_A g - m_B g \sin\beta \mp \mu m_B g \cos\beta}{m_A g + m_B g} g.$$

(a) For speed v = 0 we must use μ_s. The terms in the numerator for a are $m_A g$ = 32 lb, $m_B g \sin\beta$ = 71 lb since $\beta = \pi/4$, and $\mu_s m_B g \cos\beta$ = 40 lb. For f = 0, a < 0, indicating that if the system is stationary, block B will try to slide down the plane. Hence the force of static friction $\vec{f}$ points up the plane. If we use the maximum possible value for f, i.e. $\mu_s N$, as we have done in writing the equations of motion, we get a > 0 (lower sign in the expression for a above. Hence, in actuality $f < \mu_s N$ and a = 0 Ans.

(b) For $v \neq 0$, $\mu = \mu_k = 0.25$ so that $f = \mu_k m_B g \cos\beta$ = 18 lb. We get for the acceleration,

$$a = \frac{32 \text{ lb} - 71 \text{ lb} \mp 18 \text{ lb}}{32 \text{ lb} + 100 \text{ lb}}(32 \text{ ft/s}^2)$$

$$= -14 \text{ ft/s}^2, \text{ (B moving up plane)}$$
$$= -5.1 \text{ ft/s}^2, \text{ (B moving down plane)} \quad \text{Ans.}$$

The negative signs indicate that the acceleration is directed down the plane in both cases.

6-25

Clearly the period T of revolution is 3.14 s/3.

(a) Since the speed v is constant,

$$vT = 2\pi r \rightarrow v = 2\pi(5\ \text{cm})/(3.14\ \text{s}/3) = 30\ \text{cm/s Ans.}$$

(b) In uniform circular motion the acceleration is v^2/r. Thus,

$$a = v^2/r = (30\ \text{cm/s})^2/(5\ \text{cm}) = 1.8\ \text{m/s}^2\text{, radially inward Ans.}$$

(c) The force is just

$$F = ma = (0.002\ \text{kg})(1.8\ \text{m/s}^2) = 3.6 \times 10^{-3}\ \text{N Ans.}$$

(d) The force is provided by static friction which has a maximum value of $\mu_s N = \mu_s mg$. Therefore, since at r = 10 cm, v = 60 cm/s,

$$\mu_s mg = mv^2/r \rightarrow \mu_s = (60\ \text{cm/s})^2/(10\ \text{cm})(980\ \text{cm/s}^2) = 0.37\ \text{Ans.}$$

6-30

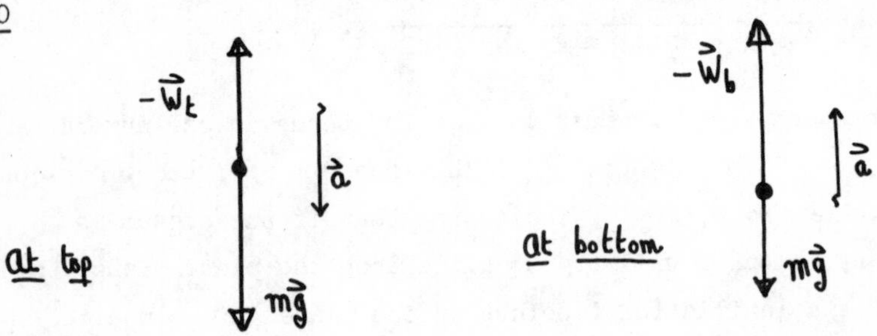

The student's acceleration is always directed to the center of the wheel. Therefore, if W denotes his apparent weight, and b = bottom, t = top,

at top: $mg - W_t = ma = mv^2/R$, at bottom: $W_b - mg = mv^2/R$,

$W_t = mg - mv^2/R$; $W_b = mg + mv^2/R$.

(a) From the equation appropriate at the top,

$$125\ \text{lb} = 150\ \text{lb} - mv^2/R \rightarrow mv^2/R = 25\ \text{lb}.$$

Hence,

$$W_b = 150\ \text{lb} + 25\ \text{lb} = 175\ \text{lb Ans.}$$

(b) If the new speed $v' = 2v$, $mv'^2/R = 4\,mv^2/R = 100$ lb. Hence now $W_b = mg - mv'^2/R = 150\ \text{lb} - 100\ \text{lb} = 50$ lb Ans.

6-34

(a)

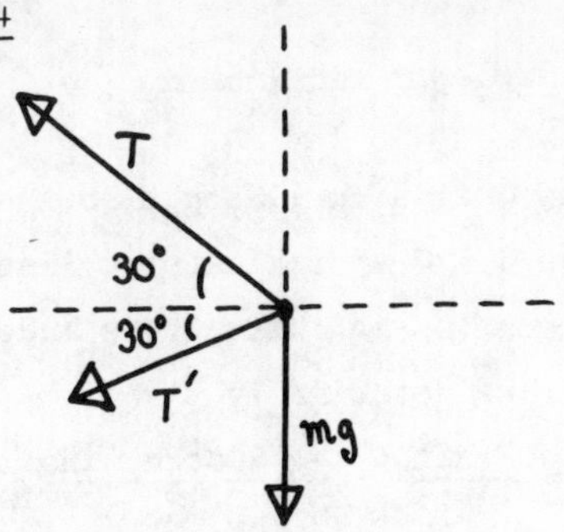

(b) The acceleration of the ball is directed horizontally toward the rod. Hence, the vertical forces sum to zero and we have,

$$T\ \sin 30° = T'\ \sin 30° + mg,$$

$$(25\ N)(0.5) = T'(0.5) + 9.8\ N,$$

$$T' = 5.4\ N\ \underline{\text{Ans.}}$$

(c) The net force $\vec{F}$ is pointed horizontally toward the rod, and its magnitude is

$$F = T\ \cos 30° + T'\cos 30° = (25 + 5.4)\frac{\sqrt{3}}{2}\ N = 26\ N\ \underline{\text{Ans.}}$$

(d) Since $F = ma = mv^2/r$, where r is the perpendicular distance of the ball from the rod, it is evident that

$$26.3\ N = \frac{(1\ kg)\ v^2}{(1\ m)\cos 30°} \rightarrow v = 4.8\ m/s\ \underline{\text{Ans.}}$$

6-36

Due to the rotation of the earth, the plumb bob is moving at constant speed in a circle of radius $R\ \cos\delta$, where R is the radius of the earth and δ is the latitude. Consequently, there must be a net force $\vec{F}$ on the bob directed at the axis of rotation. $\vec{F}$ makes an angle δ with the local vertical and has a magnitude

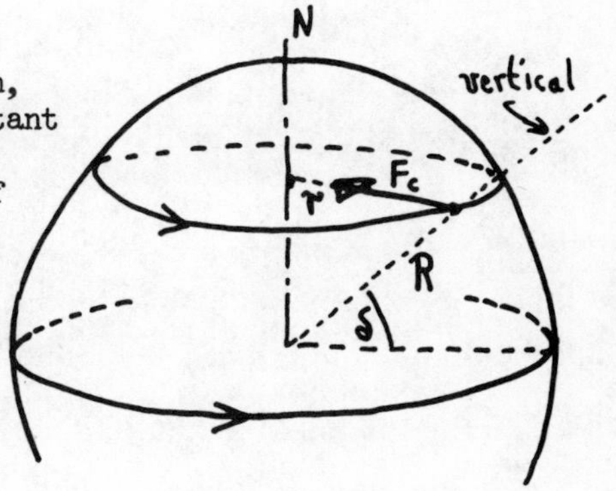

$$F = m\ \frac{v^2}{r} = m\ \frac{(2\pi R\ \cos\delta/T)^2}{R\ \cos\delta},$$

where m is the mass of the bob and T = 23 h 56 min is the rotation period of the earth.

The local situation is shown in the second figure, on the next page. Resolving into horizontal and vertical components,

$$mg - T\ \cos\alpha = F\ \cos\delta,$$

$$T\ \sin\alpha = F\ \sin\delta.$$

Transpose mg in the first equation, and then divide the second equation by the first. The result is,

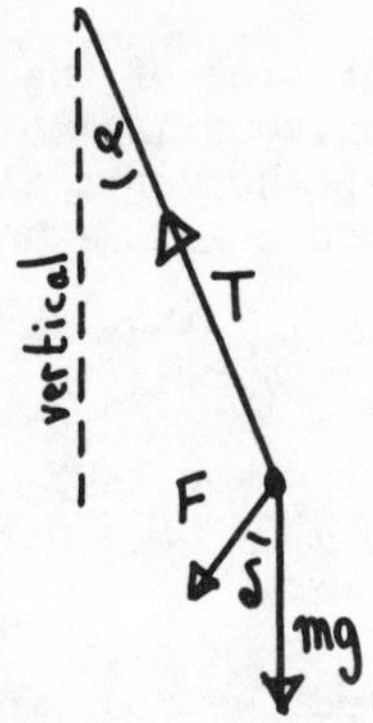

$$\tan\alpha = \frac{F\sin\delta}{mg - F\cos\delta}\,.$$

Now α is a small angle so that $\tan\alpha = \alpha$ approximately. Also $F\cos\delta \ll mg$. With these made use of, we get finally

$$\alpha = \frac{F\sin\delta}{mg} = \frac{4\pi^2 R\cos\delta\,\sin\delta}{g\,T^2}.$$

(a) With $R = 6.4 \times 10^6$ m, $g = 9.8$ m/s^2 and $\delta = 40°$ one finds $\alpha = 5.8' = 0.0017$ rad Ans.

(b),(c) At either $\delta = 0°$, or $90°$ it is clear that $\alpha = 0°$ Ans.

7-4

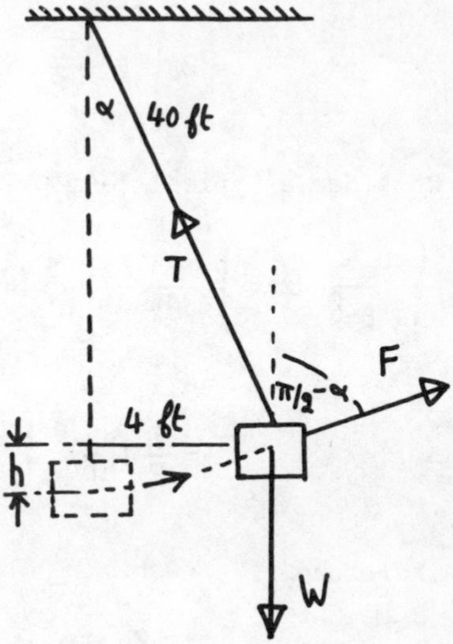

(a) For equilibrium,

$$T \cos\alpha + F \sin\alpha - W = 0,$$

$$T \sin\alpha - F \cos\alpha = 0.$$

Multiply the first equation by $\sin\alpha$, the second by $\cos\alpha$ and subtract to obtain

$$F = W \sin\alpha = (500\ \text{lb})(4/40)$$

$$F = 50\ \text{lb}\ \underline{\text{Ans}}.$$

(b) While being held in position, no work is being done since the crate is not moving, i.e. it is not undergoing a displacement.

(c) In moving it aside, the work done against gravity is W h,

$$\text{Work} = W\,h = W(L - L\cos\alpha),$$

where L is the length of the rope = 40 ft. We have then,

$$W\,h = (500\ \text{lb})(40 - 40\sqrt{1 - (4/40)^2}\ )\text{ft} = 100\ \text{ft}\cdot\text{lb}\ \underline{\text{Ans}}.$$

(d) During the displacement, the tension $\vec{T}$ is always perpendicular to the displacement, so that the work done by the tension = $\vec{T}\cdot\vec{d}$ is zero Ans.

7-5

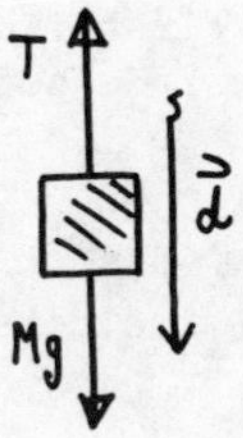

We must know the tension. Since $M\,g - T = M\,a$,

$$M\,g - T = M(g/4) \rightarrow T = \frac{3}{4}\,Mg.$$

The work done by the tension is $\vec{T}\cdot\vec{d}$ and so we get

$$W = \vec{T}\cdot\vec{d} = T\,d\cos\pi = (\frac{3}{4}\,Mg)(d)(-1) = -\frac{3}{4}\,Mgd\ \underline{\text{Ans}}.$$

7-8

We obtain the total work W by integrating dW from the initial point i to the final point f.

$$W = \int_i^f \vec{F}\cdot d\vec{r} = m\int_i^f \left(\frac{d^2x}{dt^2}\,\vec{i} + \frac{d^2y}{dt^2}\,\vec{j} + \frac{d^2z}{dt^2}\,\vec{k}\right)\cdot\left(dx\,\vec{i} + dy\,\vec{j} + dz\,\vec{k}\right)$$

$$= m\int_i^f \left(\frac{d^2x}{dt^2}\,dx + \frac{d^2y}{dt^2}\,dy + \frac{d^2z}{dt^2}\,dz\right).$$

Consider a typical term:

$$\int_i^f \frac{d^2x}{dt^2}\,dx = \int_i^f \frac{d}{dt}\left(\frac{dx}{dt}\right)dx = \int_i^f \frac{d}{dx}\left(\frac{dx}{dt}\right)\frac{dx}{dt}\,dx = \int_i^f \frac{dx}{dt}\,d\left(\frac{dx}{dt}\right)$$

$$= \frac{1}{2}\left(\frac{dx}{dt}\right)^2\Bigg|_i^f = \frac{1}{2}\left(v_x^2 - v_{x0}^2\right).$$

Therefore,

$$W = m\left[\frac{1}{2}(v_x^2 - v_{x0}^2) + \frac{1}{2}(v_y^2 - v_{y0}^2) + \frac{1}{2}(v_z^2 - v_{z0}^2)\right]$$

$$= \frac{1}{2}m\left[v_x^2 + v_y^2 + v_z^2 - (v_{x0}^2 + v_{y0}^2 + v_{z0}^2)\right] = \frac{1}{2}m\,(v^2 - v_0^2),$$

$$W = \frac{1}{2}m\,v^2 - \frac{1}{2}m\,v_0^2 \quad \underline{\text{Ans.}}$$

7-18

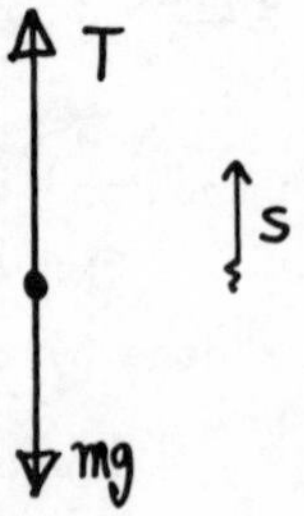

We first find the tension T in the cable. From the free-body diagram of the astronaut,

$$T - mg = ma = m(g/10) \rightarrow T = \frac{11}{10}\,mg.$$

Let the total displacement of the astronaut be $\vec{s}$.

(a) The work W done by the helicopter (i.e. by the cable) is

$$W = \vec{T}\cdot\vec{s} = (\frac{11}{10}\ mg)s = \frac{11}{10}(160\ \text{lb})(50\ \text{ft}) = 8.8 \times 10^3\ \text{ft·lb}\ \underline{\text{Ans.}}$$

(b) The work W_g done by gravity is

$$W_g = m\vec{g}\cdot\vec{s} = -\ mgs = -(160\ \text{lb})(50\ \text{ft}) = -\ 8.0 \times 10^3\ \text{ft·lb}\ \underline{\text{Ans.}}$$

(c) The net work done on the astronaut is the sum of (a) and (b), to wit, 800 ft·lb. But this is equal to the change $K_f - K_i$ in the astronaut's kinetic energy. Presumeably $K_i = 0$, so that, if v is the speed with which he reaches the helicopter,

$$800\ \text{ft·lb} = \frac{1}{2}\ m\ v^2 = \frac{1}{2}\ (\frac{160}{32}\ \text{slug})\ v^2,$$

$$v = 18\ \text{ft/s}\ \underline{\text{Ans.}}$$

7-19

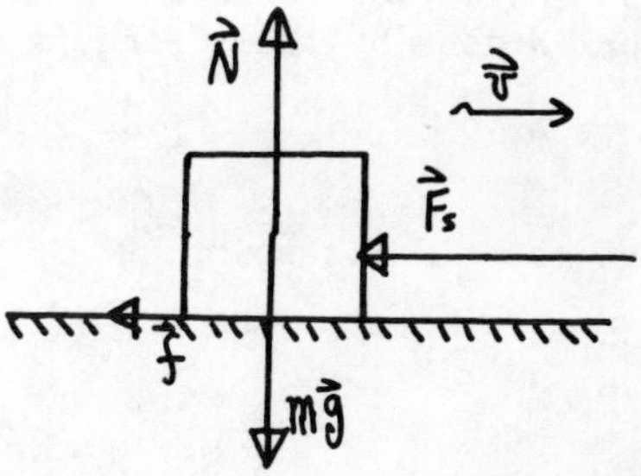

We show a free-body diagram of the block at some moment before it has been brought to rest. The spring exerts a force $\vec{F}_s$. Clearly the force of friction $\vec{f}$ is given by $f = \mu_k Mg$ since N = Mg. Also, let $\vec{L}$ be the total displacemnt of the block before being brought to rest.

(a)

$$W_f = \vec{f}\cdot\vec{L} = -\ (\mu_k Mg)L\ \underline{\text{Ans.}}$$

(b) The work done by the spring force in displacing a mass from an initial position x_i to a final position x_f is $\frac{1}{2}\ kx_i^{\ 2} - \frac{1}{2}\ kx_f^{\ 2}$. Here $x_i = 0$ and $x_f = L$. Therefore, $W_s = -\ \frac{1}{2}kL^2$ Ans.

(c) $\vec{N}$ and $M\vec{g}$ act on the block, but they are each perpendicular to the displacement of the block and hence do no work on it.

(d) The total work done is the sum of (a) and (b):

$$W_T = -\mu_k MgL - \frac{1}{2} kL^2.$$

(e) By the work-energy theorem, $W_T = \Delta K = K_f - K_i$:

$$-\mu_k MgL - \frac{1}{2} kL^2 = \Delta K = 0 - \frac{1}{2} Mv_0^2.$$

Solving the quadratic for the root with $L > 0$ we get,

$$L = \frac{1}{k} \left(\sqrt{\mu_k^2 M^2 g^2 + v_0^2 kM} - \mu_k Mg\right) \text{ \underline{Ans.}}$$

7-20

(a) The original tension is

$$T = mv^2/r = (0.675 \text{ kg})(10.0 \text{ m/s})^2/(0.5 \text{ m}) = 135 \text{ N \underline{Ans.}}$$

(b) The normal force and gravity do no work on the mass. Hence the work W done by the string in reducing the radius of the circle is

$$W = \Delta K = \frac{1}{2} mv_f^2 - \frac{1}{2} mv^2.$$

But the final tension is

$$T_f = m\, v_f^2/r_f.$$

Therefore we can write,

$$W = \frac{1}{2}(T_f r_f - T\, r).$$

Since $T_f = 4.63$ T, $r_f = 0.3$ m, $r = 0.5$ m, we have

$$W = \frac{1}{2}(135 \text{ N})\left[(4.63)(0.3 \text{ m}) - 0.5 \text{ m}\right],$$

$$W = 60.0 \text{ J \underline{Ans.}}$$

7-26

The force $\vec{F}$ applied to the tool must be directed at some angle to the radial direction in order to provide a tangential component F_t to counteract friction. The radial component F_r of F is the force actually exerted against the wheel, and this equals 40 lb. The wheel must do work against F_t; therefore

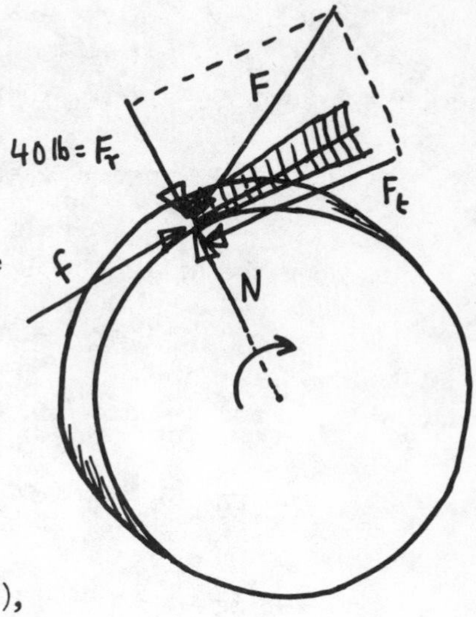

$$P = F_t v = f\ v = \mu_k F_r v.$$

But the speed v of the wheel's rim is given by

$$(2.5\ \text{rev})(2\pi)(2/3)\ \text{ft/rev} = v(1\ \text{s}),$$
$$v = 10\pi/3\ \text{ft/s}.$$

This gives

$$P = (0.32)(40\ \text{lb})(10\pi/3\ \text{ft/s}) = 134\ \text{ft}\cdot\text{lb/s}$$
$$= (134.0)/(550)\ \text{hp} = 0.24\ \text{hp}\ \underline{\text{Ans.}}$$

7-32

The force pulling the truck forward, at speed v, v', is F, F' (the primed quantities refer to motion down the hill). The resisting force in each case is F_R. In moving up or down the hill, the total work done on the truck is zero, since it is moving with constant speed in each case: $W = \Delta K = 0$. Thus, the rate at which work

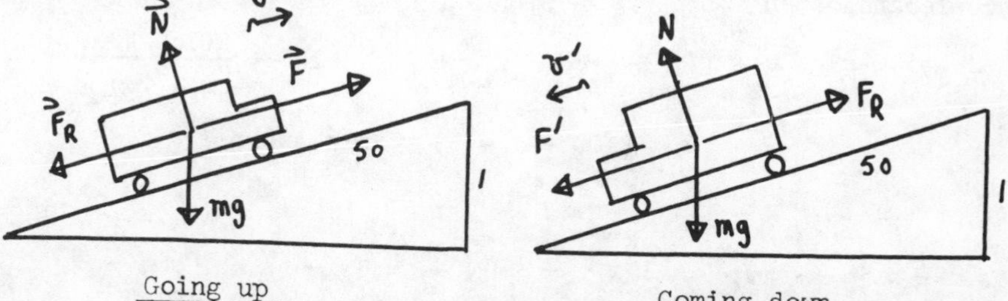

Going up   Coming down

is being done is zero also. The forces that do work are F (F'), gravity and the resisting force. Thus, for motion up the hill,

$$P - mg\,v_{up} - F_R v = 0,$$

where $P = Fv$ and $v_{up} = v/50$. Therefore,

$$P = mgv/50 + mgv/25 = \frac{3}{50}\,mgv.$$

In moving down the hill, $P' = F'v' = P = Fv$ by assumption. Hence,

$$P + mgv_d - F_R v' = 0.$$

But $v_d = v'/50$ and $P = 3mgv/50$. Therefore,

$$\frac{3}{50}\,mgv + \frac{1}{50}\,mgv' - \frac{1}{25}\,mgv' = 0.$$

$$\frac{3}{50}\,mgv = \frac{1}{50}\,mgv' \;\rightarrow\; v' = 3\,v = 3(15 \text{ mi/h}) = 45 \text{ mi/h } \underline{\text{Ans}}.$$

7-33

(a) By the work-energy theorem, neglecting rolling friction,

$$W = P\,\Delta t = (1.5 \times 10^6 \text{ W})(360 \text{ s}) = 5.4 \times 10^8 \text{ J} = \Delta K$$
$$= \tfrac{1}{2}mv_f^2 - \tfrac{1}{2}mv_i^2 = \tfrac{m}{2}\left[(25)^2 - (10)^2\right],$$

giving

$$m = 2.1 \times 10^6 \text{ kg } \underline{\text{Ans}}.$$

(b) If v is the speed at a time t after the train starts to accelerate, then

$$\frac{1}{2}\,mv^2 - \frac{1}{2}\,mv_i^2 = P\,t \;\rightarrow\; v^2 = v_i^2 + 2Pt = 100 + \frac{2(1.5 \times 10^6)}{2.1 \times 10^6}\,t,$$

$$v = (100 + 1.4\,t)^{1/2} \text{ m/s } \underline{\text{Ans}}.$$

(c) From (b),

$$\frac{1}{2}\,mv^2 - \frac{1}{2}\,mv_i^2 = P\,t \;\rightarrow\; m\,v\,\frac{dv}{dt} = P \;\rightarrow\; a = P/mv,$$

since v_i is a constant. Hence the force is

$$F = ma = P/v = P/(100 + 1.4\ t)^{1/2} = \frac{1.5 \times 10^6}{\sqrt{(100 + 1.4\ t)}}\ \text{N}$$ <u>Ans.</u>

(d) The total distance is

$$x = \int v(t)dt = \int_0^{360} (100 + 1.4\ t)^{1/2}\ dt = 6.9 \times 10^3\ \text{m} = 6.9\ \text{km}$$ <u>Ans.</u>

CHAPTER 8

8-3

The minimum work W required is that performed by exerting a force F on the chain just equal to the weight of chain still hanging over the table's edge. If at some instant a length x is hanging over, then $F(x) = (m/L)gx$. Since the chain is being displaced in a way so that x decreases, we have

$$W = -\int F\,dx = -\int_{L/5}^{0} (m/L)gx\,dx = mgL/50 \text{ Ans.}$$

8-6

We show the 'initial' and 'final' positions of the block in a diagram, with the zero-level of gravitational potential energy clearly marked. In both of these positions, the velocity and hence kinetic energy of the mass is zero. By conservation of energy, with U_s being the potential energy of the spring,

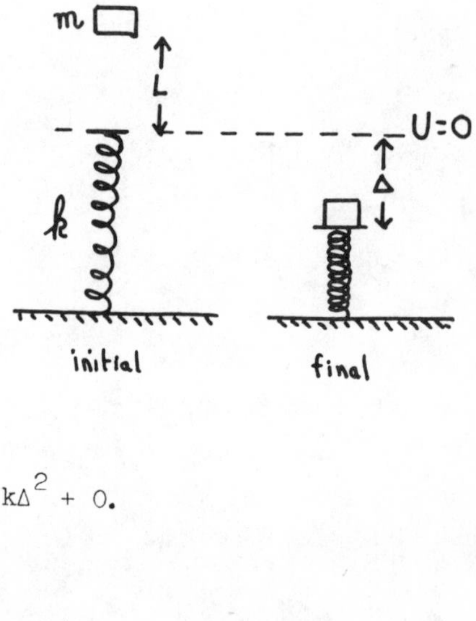

$$U_i + U_{si} + K_i = U_f + U_{sf} + K_f,$$

$$mg(+L) + \frac{1}{2}k(0)^2 + 0 = mg(-\Delta) + \frac{1}{2}k\Delta^2 + 0.$$

This can be rearranged to give,

$$\Delta^2 - (2mg/k)\Delta - (2mgL/k) = 0.$$

But $mg/k = (2\text{ kg})(9.8\text{ m/s}^2)/(1960\text{ N/m}) = 0.01\text{ m}$; $mgL/k = 0.004\text{ m}^2$. With these substitutions the equation becomes,

$$\Delta^2 - (0.02)\Delta - 0.008 = 0 \rightarrow \Delta = 0.10\text{ m Ans.}$$

8-9

Note that

$$1 \text{ ton} = 2000 \text{ lb} = 8900 \text{ N}, \quad 30 \text{ ft} = 9.14 \text{ m}.$$

(a) The energy required is

$$E = mgh = Wh = (8900 \text{ N})(9.14 \text{ m}) = 81300 \text{ J}.$$

Since 1 kW·hr = 36×10^5 J, this energy represents $81300/36 \times 10^5$ $= 2.3 \times 10^{-2}$ kW·hr Ans.

(b) Since 12 hr contains (12)(3600) s, the average power is

$$\overline{P} = (81300 \text{ J})/(12)(3600 \text{ s}) = 1.9 \text{ W} \text{ Ans.}$$

8-19

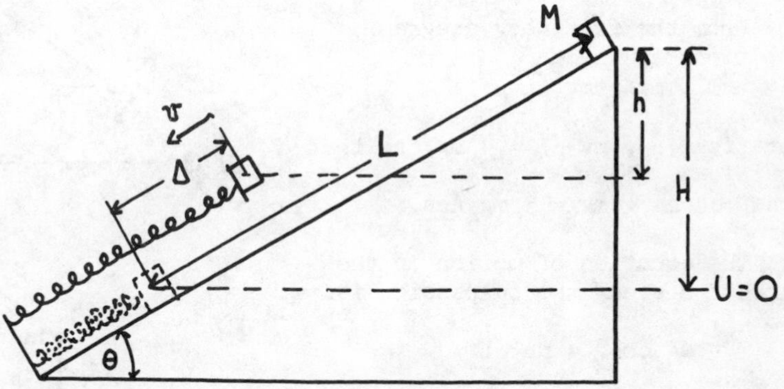

Since $F_s = kx \rightarrow 100 \text{ N} = k(1.0 \text{ m}) \rightarrow k = 100$ N/m. We show clearly our reference level $U = 0$ for gravitational potential energy. Let L = total distance the mass slides before being brought momentarily to rest.

(a) By the conservation of energy,

$$U_i + U_{si} + K_i = U_f + U_{sf} + K_f \rightarrow mg(+H) + 0 + 0 = 0 + \frac{1}{2} k\Delta^2 + 0.$$

Solving this for H gives $H = k\Delta^2/2mg$. Numerically this is

$$H = (100\ \text{N/m})(2\ \text{m})^2/2(10\ \text{kg})(9.8\ \text{m/s}^2) = 2.04\ \text{m}.$$

Now $L = H \csc\theta = (2.04\ \text{m})(2) = 4.08$ m Ans, since $\theta = \pi/6$.

(b) Clearly $h = H - \Delta \sin\theta = 2.04 - (2)(1/2) = 1.04$ m. But, again by conservation of energy,

$$mgh = \frac{1}{2} mv^2 \rightarrow v = \sqrt{(2)(9.8\ \text{m/s}^2)(1.04\ \text{m})} = 4.5\ \text{m/s Ans.}$$

8-21

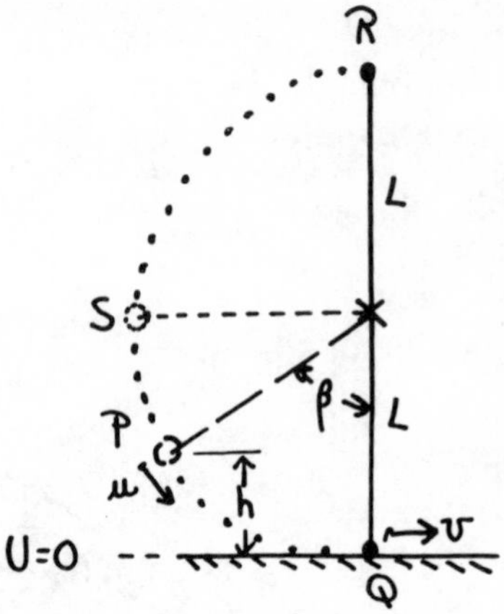

By conservation of energy,

$$U_R + K_R = U_Q + K_Q,$$

$$mg(2L) + 0 = 0 + \frac{1}{2} mv^2,$$

$$v = 2\sqrt{gL}\ \text{Ans.}$$

(b) From the free-body diagram,

$$T - mg = mv^2/L$$

But from (a), $mv^2/L = 4$ mg, so that

$$T = 4\ mg + mg = 5\ mg\ \text{Ans.}$$

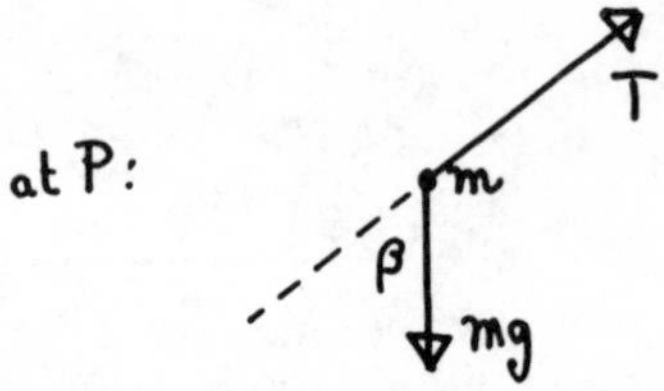

(c) The equation of motion in the direction along the suspension is,

$$T - mg\cos\beta = mu^2/L.$$

But, from energy conservation, $U_S + K_S = U_P + K_P$,

$$mgL + 0 = mgh + \frac{1}{2} mu^2,$$

$$\rightarrow u^2 = 2gL\cos\beta,$$

since $h = L - L\cos\beta$. Hence the tension is

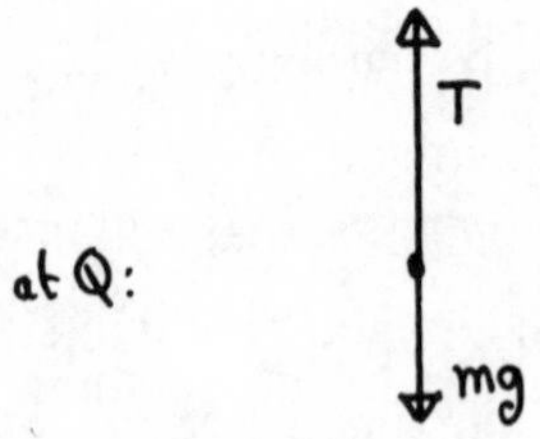

$$T = 2mg\cos\beta + mg\cos\beta = 3mg\cos\beta.$$

If $T = mg$, $\cos\beta = 1/3$ or $\beta = 71°$ Ans.

8-24

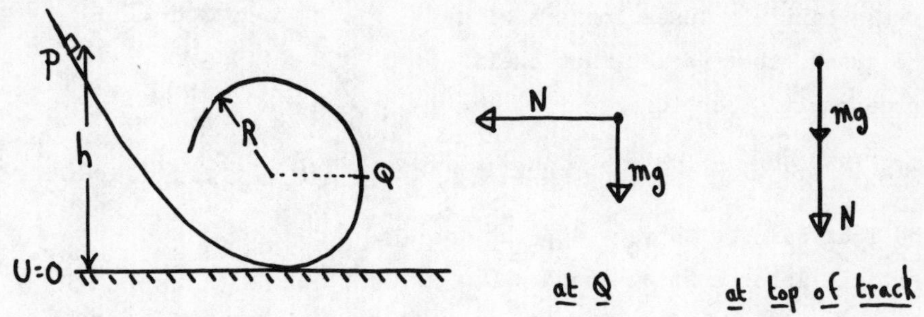

With the track frictionless, we can apply conservation of energy. Shown in our diagram is the reference level for potential energy; also given are free-body diagrams of the block when at Q and at the top of the track.

(a)

$$mgh + 0 = mg(R) + \frac{1}{2} mv_Q^2 \rightarrow mv_Q^2/R = 8\ mg,$$

since h = 5 R. Thus the forces are mg down, and 8mg to the left Ans.

(b) At the top of the track,

$$N + mg = mv_t^2/R,$$

where v_t is the speed at the top. But, by energy conservation,

$$mgh + 0 = mg(2R) + \frac{1}{2} mv_t^2.$$

Now we want N = mg. By the first equation, this implies that $\frac{1}{2} mv_t^2 = mgR$. Substituting this into the second equation yields

$$mgh + 0 = mg(2R) + mgR \rightarrow h = 3R \text{ Ans.}$$

8-26

(a) At the top, Newton's second law and energy conservation require,

$$N + mg = mv^2/R, \qquad \frac{1}{2} mv_0^2 + 0 = \frac{1}{2} mv^2 + mg(2R).$$

Combining these,

$$mv_0^2/R = N + 5\ mg.$$

If $v_0 = v_m$, $N \to 0$ at the top, since if the particle loses contact with the track, the track cannot exert a force on it. Therefore,

$$mv_m^2/R = 5mg \quad \to \quad v_m = \sqrt{5gR} \ \underline{\text{Ans.}}$$

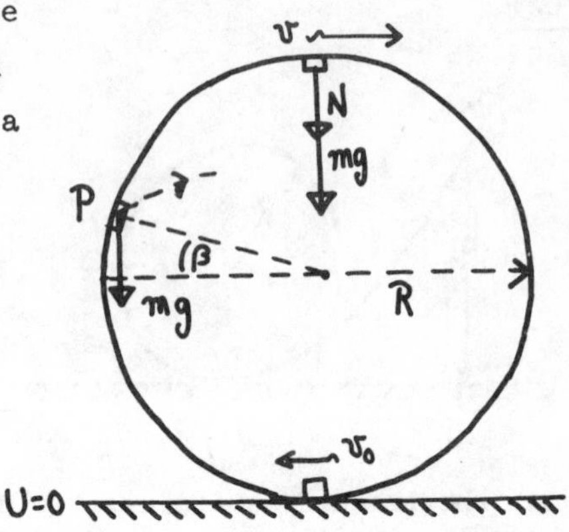

(b) This time, with $v_0 < v_m$, the particle loses contact and $N \to 0$ at some point P before the top is reached. Again, by Newton's second law and energy conservation,

$$mg\,\sin\beta = mv_p^2/R, \qquad \frac{1}{2}mv_0^2 + 0 = \frac{1}{2}mv_p^2 + mg(R + R\,\sin\beta).$$

Eliminating v_p,

$$mg\,\sin\beta = mv_0^2/R - 2mg(1 + \sin\beta) \quad \to \quad 3g\,\sin\beta = \frac{v_0^2}{R} - 2\,g,$$

$$3g\,\sin\beta = [(0.775)(\sqrt{5gR})]^2/R - 2g = g,$$

$$\beta = \sin^{-1}(1/3) \ \underline{\text{Ans.}}$$

8-27

If the ball just swings around the nail, the tension $T \to 0$ at the uppermost point. By Newton's second law and energy conservation,

$$mu^2/(L - d) = mg,$$

$$mgL + 0 = mg\,2(L - d) + \frac{1}{2}mu^2,$$

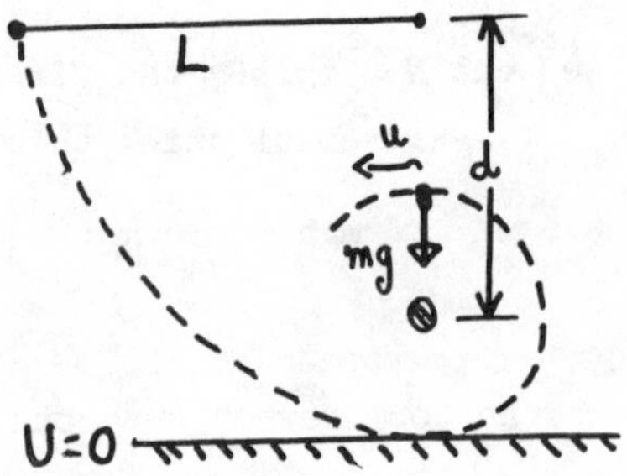

where u is the speed at the top. Eliminating u between these equations gives

$$d = \frac{3}{5}L \ \underline{\text{Ans.}}$$

8-29

(a) Each second the escalator does work $W = mgh$, where

$$m = (100/60 \text{ persons})(5 \text{ slug/person}) = 50/6 \text{ slug}.$$

The power delivered is

$$P = W/t = (50/6 \text{ slug/s})(32 \text{ ft/s}^2)(25 \text{ ft}) = 6700 \text{ ft}\cdot\text{lb/s} \ \underline{\text{Ans.}}$$

(b) If the man did not walk the escalator would carry him up in (40 ft)/(2 ft/s) = 20 s. Since he reaches the top in 10 s, the escalator does one-half the required work, that is,

$$\frac{1}{2} W = \frac{1}{2} (160 \text{ lb})(25 \text{ ft}) = 2000 \text{ ft}\cdot\text{lb} \ \underline{\text{Ans.}}$$

(c) Under these conditions, the man is not moving and his displacement is thereby zero; hence $W = 0$ Ans.

(d) If the man walks faster or slower than in (c) he will suffer a downward or upward vertical displacement respectively. In these cases the escalator will do negative or positive work, respectively, on him. Thus the answer is no.

8-30

(a) We expect the string to stretch under the centrifugal forces that develop as a result of the circular motion.

(b) Let $U = 0$ at the bottom of the swing. Energy conservation and Newton's second law require, respectively,

$$mg(L + \Delta L) = \frac{1}{2} mv^2 + \frac{1}{2} k(\Delta L)^2,$$

$$k(\Delta L) - mg = mv^2/(L + \Delta L),$$

where v is the speed at the bottom. Eliminating this quantity gives

$$\frac{3}{2} mgL(1 + \frac{\Delta L}{L}) = \frac{1}{2} kL^2(\frac{\Delta L}{L})\left[1 + 2(\frac{\Delta L}{L})\right].$$

If $\Delta L/L \ll 1$, this equation becomes

$$\frac{3}{2}\,mgL = \frac{1}{2}\,kL^2\left(\frac{\Delta L}{L}\right) \;\rightarrow\; \Delta L = 3\;mg/k\;\underline{\text{Ans.}}$$

(c) From the force equation,

$$v^2 = \frac{kL}{m}\left(1 + \frac{\Delta L}{L}\right)\Delta L - gL\left(1 + \frac{\Delta L}{L}\right) = \frac{kL}{m}\,\Delta L - gL - g\,\Delta L,$$

the last step only if $\Delta L/L \ll 1$, as we are assuming. Putting in the result from (a) for ΔL leads to,

$$v^2 = 2g\left(L - \frac{3mg}{2k}\right).$$

Evidently, some of the original gravitational potential energy of the system ends up as potential energy of the stretched string, leaving less for kinetic energy.

8-38

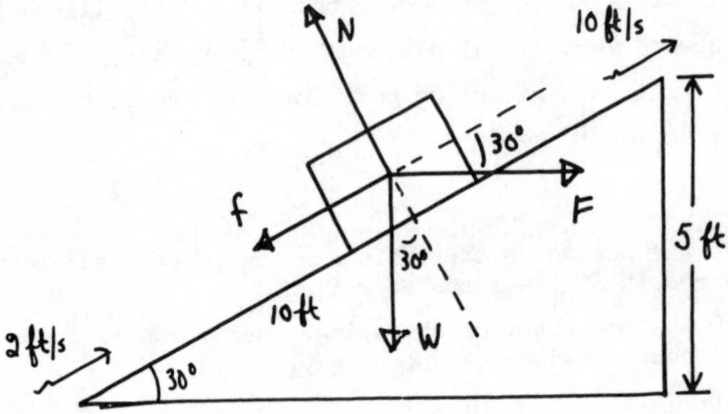

The mass of the body is (40 lb)/(32 ft/s^2) = 1.25 slug.

(a) By the work-energy theorem, since only gravity and the force $\vec{F}$ do work on the body (the track is frictionless in this part),

$$\frac{1}{2}(1.25\text{ slug})(10^2 - 2^2)\text{ft}^2/\text{s}^2 = -(40\text{ lb})(10\text{ ft})(\sin 30°) + W_F,$$

$$W_F = +\,260\text{ ft}\cdot\text{lb}\;\underline{\text{Ans}},$$

since $\sin 30° = 1/2$.

(b) We found $W_F = + 260$ ft·lb. But from the figure,

$$W_F = F\ (10\ \text{ft})(\cos 30^\circ) = +\ 260\ \text{ft·lb} \rightarrow F = 30.0\ \text{lb}\ \underline{\text{Ans.}}$$

(c) Apply the work-energy theorem. Friction is now present and does work on the body. Let L be the distance the body moves before coming to rest.

$$0 - \tfrac{1}{2}(1.25\ \text{slug})(2\ \text{ft/s})^2 = W_g + W_f + W_F.$$

The work W_g done by gravity is $W_g = -(40\ \text{lb})(L/2) = -\ 20\ L$ ft·lb.
The work W_F done by $\vec{F}$ is $W_F = +(30.0\ \text{lb})(L\sqrt{3}/2) = +\ 25.98$ ft·lb.
The work W_f done by friction is $W_f = -\mu_k N\ L$. But,

$$N = W \cos 30^\circ + F \sin 30^\circ = 49.6\ \text{lb}.$$

Therefore $W_f = -(0.15)(49.6\ \text{lb})L = -\ 7.44\ L$ ft·lb. Putting W_g, W_F and W_f into the right-hand side of the equation above gives

$$-\ 2.50 = -\ 20\ L - 7.44\ L + 25.98\ L \rightarrow L = 1.7\ \text{ft}\ \underline{\text{Ans.}}$$

<u>8-41</u>

(a) Let F be the friction force = 1000 lb. The mass of the elevator is $m = (4000\ \text{lb})/(32\ \text{ft/s}^2) = 125$ slug. Then, by the work-energy theorem,

$$\frac{1}{2}\,mv^2 - 0 = mg(12\ \text{ft}) - F(12\ \text{ft}) = 36 \times 10^3\ \text{ft·lb},$$

$$v = 24\ \text{ft/s}\ \underline{\text{Ans.}}$$

(b) The elevator comes momentarily to rest; therefore,

$$0 - \frac{1}{2}\,mv^2 = mgs - \frac{1}{2}\,ks^2 - Fs,$$

since the spring does negative work, trying to push the elevator up the shaft as it moves downward. We get

$$-\ 36{,}000\ \text{ft·lb} = (4000\ \text{lb})s - \tfrac{1}{2}(10{,}000\ \text{lb/ft})s^2 - (1000\ \text{lb})s,$$

$$5s^2 - 3s - 36 = 0 \rightarrow s = 3 \text{ ft } \underline{\text{Ans.}}$$

(c) Since the spring only extends s = 3 ft,

$$0 - 0 = - mgx + \frac{1}{2} ks^2 - Fx \rightarrow x = 9 \text{ ft } \underline{\text{Ans}},$$

after substituting numerical values.

(d) Gravity and the spring force are conservative forces. Hence, all of the energy of the system is dissipated by friction. If we can neglect static friction, the spring will be compressed a distance Δ when the elevator finally comes to rest where $k\Delta = mg$, or $\Delta = (4000 \text{ lb})/(10{,}000 \text{ lb/ft}) = 0.4$ ft. The total energy of the system the instant the cabled snapped is

$$E_i = (4000 \text{ lb})(12 \text{ ft} + 0.4 \text{ ft}) = 49.6 \times 10^3 \text{ ft·lb},$$

taking the final position as the U = 0 level. The final energy is

$$E_f = \frac{1}{2} k\Delta^2 = \frac{1}{2}(10{,}000 \text{ lb/ft})(0.4 \text{ ft})^2 = 800 \text{ ft·lb}.$$

The difference was removed by friction doing work on the elevator. If the elevator moved a total distance y we have

$$(49.6 \times 10^3 - 800)\text{ft·lb} = F\,y = (1000 \text{ lb})\,y,$$

$$y = 49 \text{ ft } \underline{\text{Ans.}}$$

The answer is exact to the extent we can neglect the role of friction in determining the elevator's final position.

<u>8-48</u>

(a) Relativistically, $m = m_0/(1 - \beta^2)^{1/2}$ with $\beta = v/c$. We have $m_0 = 0.010$ kg and $\beta = 3 \times 10^7/3 \times 10^8 = 0.1$ in one case, and $\beta = 2.7 \times 10^8/3 \times 10^8 = 0.9$ in the other. By direct substitution,

$$m = 0.01005 \text{ kg } (\beta = 0.1), \qquad m = 0.023 \text{ kg } (\beta = 0.9) \ \underline{\text{Ans.}}$$

(b) Classically $K = \frac{1}{2} m_0 v^2 = \frac{1}{2} m_0 \beta^2 c^2$. Again, by direct substitution

$$K = 4.5 \times 10^{12} \text{ J } (\beta = 0.1), \qquad K = 3.6 \times 10^{14} \text{ J } (\beta = 0.9) \text{ Ans.}$$

In the relativistic calculation, $K = (m - m_0)c^2$. Using the results from (a) we get,

$$K = 4.5 \times 10^{12} \text{ J } (\beta = 0.1), \qquad K = 1.2 \times 10^{15} \text{ J } (\beta = 0.9) \text{ Ans.}$$

(c) In this case $v = 0$, and therefore $m = m_0 = 0.010$ kg; also $K = 0$ both classically and relativistically Ans.

8-49

(a) Since

$$m = m_0(1 - v^2/c^2)^{-1/2} \rightarrow v^2 = c^2\left(1 - \frac{m_0^2}{m^2}\right).$$

Therefore

$$K = (m - m_0)c^2 = (m - m_0)v^2/(1 - m_0^2/m^2) = \frac{m^2 v^2}{m + m_0}.$$

(b) For the usual expression,

$$K = (m - m_0)c^2 = m_0\left(\frac{1}{\sqrt{1 - \beta^2}} - 1\right)c^2 = m_0\left(1 + \frac{1}{2}\beta^2 + \dots - 1\right)c^2$$

$$\rightarrow K = \frac{1}{2} m_0 \beta^2 c^2 = \frac{1}{2} m_0 v^2.$$

For the new expression, as $m \rightarrow m_0$,

$$K = \frac{m^2 v^2}{m_0 + m} \rightarrow K = m_0^2 v^2/(m_0 + m_0) = \frac{1}{2} m_0 v^2.$$

<u>9-6</u>

It is easiest to perform the integrations in polar coordinates. Clearly $x_{cm} = 0$ by symmetry. For the y-coordinate,

$$My_{cm} = \int y\ dm$$

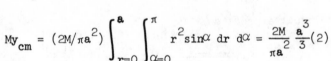

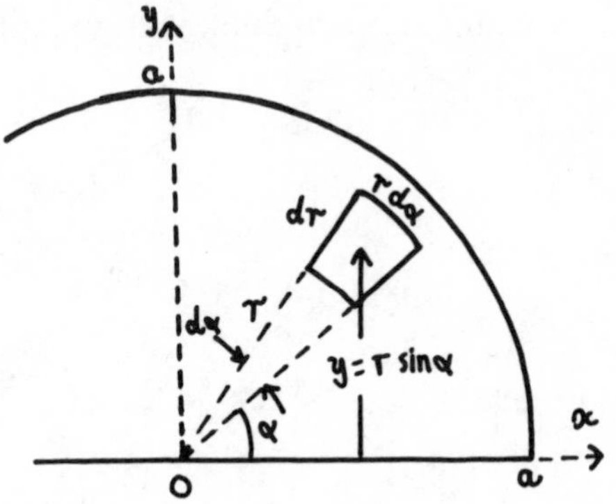

where $dm = \rho\, dA = \rho\, r\ dr\ d\alpha$. Since the density $\rho = M/(\frac{1}{2}\pi a^2)$ we have

$$dm = (2M/\pi a^2) r\ dr\ d\alpha.$$

Substituting into the first equation gives

$$My_{cm} = \int (r \sin\alpha)\ dm,$$

$$My_{cm} = (2M/\pi a^2) \int_{r=0}^{a} \int_{\alpha=0}^{\pi} r^2 \sin\alpha\ dr\ d\alpha = \frac{2M}{\pi a^2} \frac{a^3}{3}(2)$$

$$\rightarrow\ y_{cm} = 4a/3\pi \quad \underline{\text{Ans.}}$$

<u>9-9</u>

(a) Before the man starts to move the momentum of the system (man + balloon) is zero; it must remain zero while he is moving because no net external forces act on the system. Thus the balloon will move down at some speed v_B. The velocity of the man with respect to the earth is $v - v_B$, and from conservation of momentum we can write

$$m(v - v_B) = M\,v_B \quad \rightarrow \quad v_B = \frac{m}{m + M}\,v \text{ Ans.}$$

(b) After the man stops climbing the balloon is again stationary, since the total momentum must be zero.

9-14

With the ice being frictionless, the center of mass of (iceboat + man) must move with constant velocity even though the man changes his position relative to the iceboat.

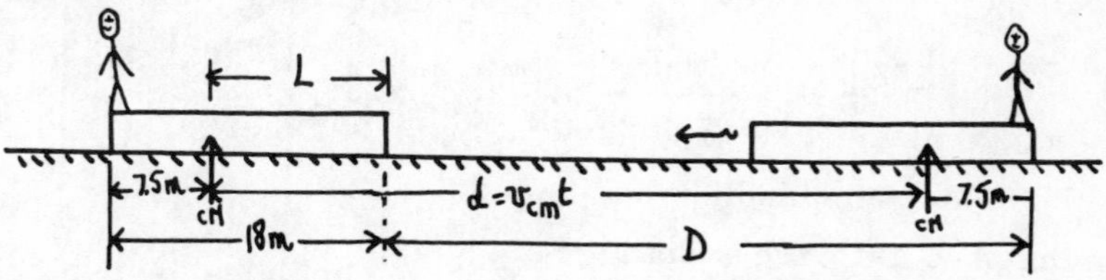

The center of mass of (man + boat) is at a distance

$$\frac{(80\text{ kg})(0\text{ m}) + (400\text{ kg})(9\text{ m})}{(400 + 80)\text{kg}} = 7.5\text{ m}$$

from the end on which the man is standing, before and after his walk. The man takes a time $t = (18\text{ m})/(2\text{ m/s}) = 9$ s to walk from one end of the boat to the other. In that time, the center of mass moves across the ice a distance

$$d = v_{cm}t = (4\text{ m/s})(9\text{ s}) = 36\text{ m}.$$

The distance D that the boat moved, measured, say, by the motion of the end of the boat (see figure) is

$$D = 7.5 + d - L = 7.5 + 36 - (18 - 7.5) = 33\text{ m Ans.}$$

9-18

(a) Clearly, the center of mass lies midway between the bodies Ans.

(b) Let x_1, x_2 be the distance of the center of mass from the 520 g, 480 g body, respectively. Then, since $x_1 + x_2 = 5$ cm, and $(520\text{ g})x_1 = (480\text{ g})x_2$ we get $x_1 = 2.4$ cm, or center of mass has moved 0.1 cm closer to the greater mass Ans.

(c) We know that

$$(m_1 + m_2)a_{cm} = F_{ext}.$$

The external forces are shown in the figure: i.e. the weights of the bodies and a force 2T acting at the pulley's support. Hence,

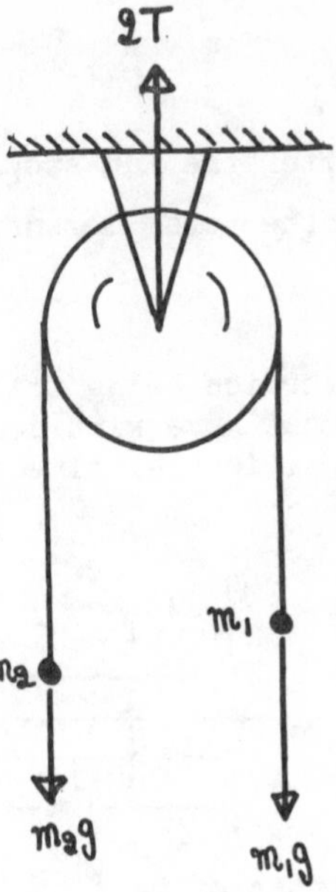

$$(m_1 + m_2)a_{cm} = (m_1 + m_2)g - 2T.$$

To determine 2T, apply F = ma to each body to obtain,

$$\left.\begin{array}{l} m_1g - T = m_1a, \\ T - m_2g = m_2a, \end{array}\right\} 2T = \frac{4m_1m_2}{m_1 + m_2} g.$$

Putting this into the second equation gives a_{cm}:

$$a_{cm} = \left[1 - \frac{4m_1m_2}{(m_1 + m_2)^2}\right] g = 0.0016\ g\ \underline{\text{Ans}},$$

after substituting numerical values for m_1 and m_2.

9-21

The average force F exerted by the bullets on the gun is, if n = the number of bullets fired each second,

$$F = \frac{n\ m\ v}{(1\ s)} \rightarrow 180\ N = n\ (50 \times 10^{-3}\ kg)(1000\ m/s),$$

$$n = 3.6\ s^{-1}.$$

Thus the number fired per minute is $(3.6)(60) = 220\ min^{-1}$ Ans.

9-22

The force N exerted by the table is,

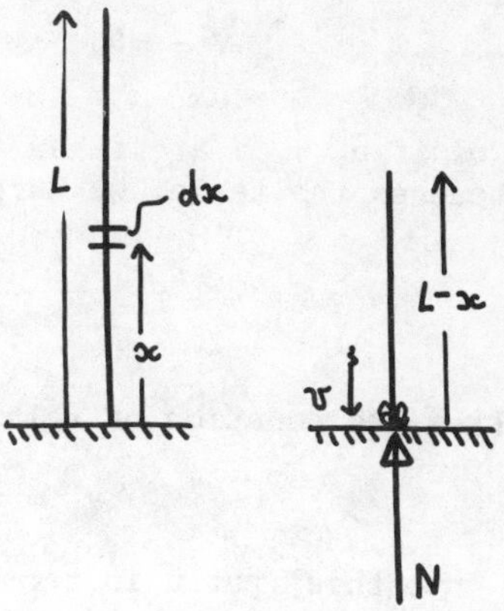

N = weight of chain already on table $+ \frac{dp}{dt}$ of link just landing,

$$N = \frac{M}{L} xg + \frac{dp}{dt} .$$

Let dM be the mass, and dx the length, of each link. Then,

$$dp/dt = (dM)v/dt = (\frac{M}{L}\ dx\ v)/dt$$

$$= \frac{M}{L} v^2 = \frac{M}{L}\ 2gx,$$

x being the original height above the table of the link just landing. Therefore N becomes

$$N = \frac{M}{L} xg + 2\frac{M}{L} xg = 3(\frac{M}{L} x)g = 3 \times \text{(weight of chain on table)}$$ Ans.

9-29

Let

$\vec{V}$ = velocity of wedge wrt table,

$\vec{u}$ = velocity of block wrt wedge,

$\vec{v}$ = velocity of block wrt table.

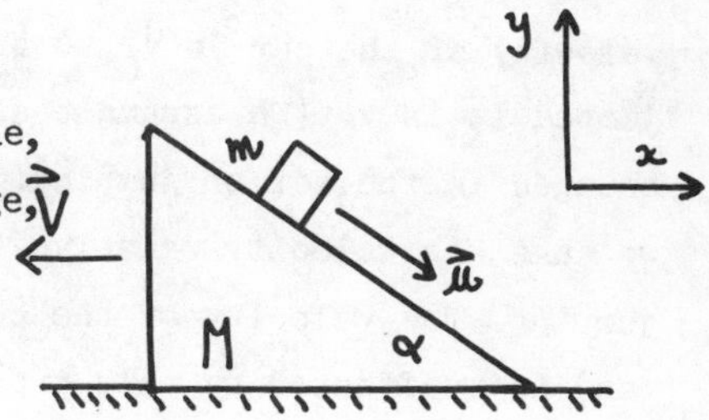

Then we have $\vec{u} + \vec{V} = \vec{v}$.

Now the block remains in contact with the wedge, so that

$$\vec{u} = u\cos\alpha\ \vec{i} - u\sin\alpha\ \vec{j},$$

and therefore, since $\vec{V} = -V\vec{i}$,

$$\vec{v} = (u\cos\alpha - V)\vec{i} - u\sin\alpha\ \vec{j}.$$

Momentum is conserved in the horizontal direction:

$$M\,V = m(u\cos\alpha - V) \;\rightarrow\; V = \frac{mu\cos\alpha}{m + M}\,. \qquad (1)$$

Now if u, v, V are taken as applying at the moment the block touches the table, we have from conservation of energy,

$$mgh = \frac{1}{2}MV^2 + \frac{1}{2}mv^2. \qquad (2)$$

From the equation of relative motion we have

$$v^2 = u^2 + V^2 - 2uV\cos\alpha.$$

Into this, put u in terms of V from (1), and then v in terms of V from (2) and solve for V: one obtains

$$V^2 = \frac{2ghm^2\cos^2\alpha}{(m + M)\left[(m + M) - m\cos^2\alpha\right]} \quad \underline{\text{Ans.}}$$

9-36

First we solve for the change in speed for only one man on the flatcar, who jumps off in the prescribed manner. Initially, the velocity of the car is v_0 to the right, say, and after the man has jumped it is v. (We assume that the velocity of the car is not changed in the act of jumping.) Then, since the man runs to the left we take his velocity relative to the ground to be $v - v_{rel}$ after jumping. The velocity of the center of mass of the system (car + man) is unaffected by this process: hence,

$$v_{cm} = v_0 = \frac{Wv + w(v - v_{rel})}{W + w} \;\rightarrow\; \Delta v = v - v_0 = \frac{wv_{rel}}{w + W}.$$

(i) Now if there are n men and all go at once, use the result above with w replaced by nw:

$$\Delta v_i = \frac{nwv_{rel}}{W + nw}.$$

(ii) If the n men go in sucession, we calculate the increment in speed imparted by each. For the first man,

$$\Delta v_1 = \frac{wv_{rel}}{w + [W + (n - 1)w]}$$

since the original flatcar is now, essentially, replaced by the flatcar + the (n - 1) men who stay behind. Thus we get for the total change in speed $\Delta v_{ii} = \Delta v_1 + \ldots + \Delta v_n$,

$$\Delta v_{ii} = \frac{w\, v_{rel}}{W + nw}\left[1 + \frac{W + nw}{W + (n - 1)w} + \ldots + \frac{W + nw}{W + w}\right]$$

after multiplying top and bottom by (W + nw) and factoring out wv_{rel}. Now all the terms in the brackets are $\geqslant 1$ and there are n of them. Hence the second method yields a greater change in speed than the first: i.e. $\Delta v_{ii} > \Delta v_i$ Ans.

9-38

Since the coal leaves the slow barge in a direction perpendicular to its velocity, the reaction it imparts is perpendicular to $\vec{v}_0$. Therefore, no additional force is required.

The coal arrives on the faster barge with a velocity component parallel to the barge's motion, equal to (20 - 10) = 10 km/h, opposite to the barge's velocity. Hence, the additional force required is

$$F = v_{rel}\frac{dm}{dt} = (10 \text{ km/h})(1000 \text{ kg/min}) = 46 \text{ N} \quad \text{Ans.}$$

9-39

(a) In taking in the air, the plane experiences a resisting force F_1 equal to

$$F_1 = v_{rel}\frac{dm}{dt} = (600 \text{ ft/s})(4.8 \text{ slug/s}) = 2880 \text{ lb.}$$

The mass ejected each second is the 4.8 slug of air plus 0.2 slug of fuel. The thrust imparted to the plane in ejecting this mass is

$$F_2 = v_{rel}\frac{dm}{dt} = (1600 \text{ ft/s})(5 \text{ slug/s}) = 8000 \text{ lb.}$$

The net thrust is

$$F = F_2 - F_1 = 8000 \text{ lb} - 2880 \text{ lb} = 5120 \text{ lb } \underline{\text{Ans.}}$$

(b) The horsepower delivered is

$$P = F\,v = (5120 \text{ lb})(600 \text{ ft/s})/(550 \text{ ft}\cdot\text{lb/s}\cdot\text{hp}),$$

$$P = 5600 \text{ hp } \underline{\text{Ans.}}$$

<u>9-41</u>

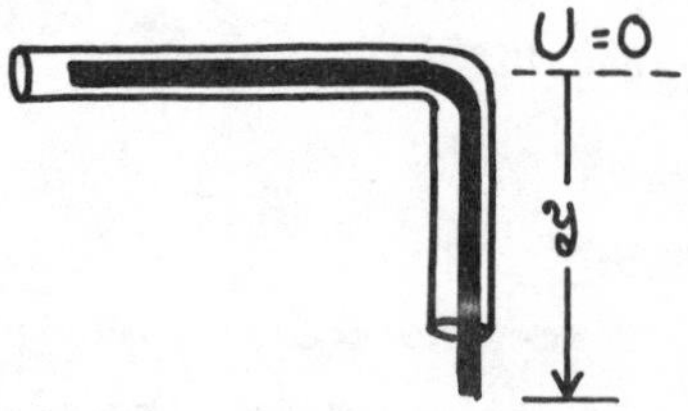

(a) Considering the string as the system, its mass is not changing and therefore $v_{rel} = 0$. Now let γ be the mass per unit length of the string.

(b) The force accelerating the string is $(\gamma y)g$, but since the whole string accelerates the equation of motion will be

$$\gamma y g = \gamma L\ddot{y} \rightarrow L\,\ddot{y} - gy = 0 \ \underline{\text{Ans.}}$$

(c) The kinetic and potential energies are

$$K = \frac{1}{2}(\gamma L)\dot{y}^2, \quad U = -(\gamma y)g\,\frac{y}{2} = -\frac{1}{2}\gamma g y^2.$$

With the tube frictionless, K + U = constant; write the constant as $C\gamma/2$: then

$$K + U = \frac{1}{2}C\gamma \rightarrow \frac{1}{2}\gamma L\dot{y}^2 - \frac{1}{2}\gamma g y^2 = \frac{1}{2}C\gamma \rightarrow L\dot{y}^2 - gy^2 = C.$$

Differentiating this with repect to time yields the equation of motion quoted in (b).

(d) The given solution can be verified by direct substitution; it is valid only until $y = L$.

CHAPTER 10

10-4

Let the downward direction be positive. Then,

(a) $J = m(v_f - v_i) = (1.0 \text{ kg})[(-10 \text{ m/s}) - (+25 \text{ m/s})]$,

$$J = -35 \text{ N·s} \quad \text{(i.e. upward) } \underline{\text{Ans.}}$$

(b) $J = \bar{F}\,\Delta t \rightarrow \bar{F} = J/\Delta t = (-35 \text{ N·s})/(0.020 \text{ s})$,

$$\bar{F} = -1750 \text{ N (i.e. upward) } \underline{\text{Ans.}}$$

10-10

With v_{12}, v_{18} the final speeds we have, since the initial momentum of each spacecraft is zero,

$$m_{12}v_{12} = m_{18}v_{18}, \qquad m_{12}v_{12} + m_{18}v_{18} = 600 \text{ N·s}.$$

Putting $m_{12} = 1200$ kg and $m_{18} = 1800$ kg, the final speeds are found to be $v_{12} = 1/4$ m/s, $v_{18} = 1/6$ m/s. Since the spacecraft go off in opposite directions the relative speed is

$$v = v_{12} + v_{18} = \frac{1}{4} + \frac{1}{6} = \frac{5}{12} \text{ m/s } \underline{\text{Ans.}}$$

10-18

Let the required height be h. If v is the speed of m_1 just before collision,

$$m_1 gd = \frac{1}{2} m_1 v^2 \rightarrow v = \sqrt{2\,gd}\ .$$

Also, if v' is the speed of the combination just after collision,

$$m_1 v + 0 = (m_1 + m_2)v' \rightarrow v' = \frac{m_1}{m_1 + m_2}\sqrt{2gd}.$$

Applying conservation of energy to the combination after collision,

$$(m_1 + m_2)gh = \frac{1}{2}(m_1 + m_2)v'^2.$$

Replacing v' with the expression given above and solving for h gives

$$h = d\left(\frac{m_1}{m_1 + m_2}\right)^2 \text{ Ans.}$$

10-24

By conservation of momentum and mechanical energy,

$$mv_i = (m + M)V,$$

$$\frac{1}{2} mv_i^2 = \frac{1}{2}(m + M)V^2 + U_s = \frac{1}{2}(m + M)V^2 + f\,\frac{1}{2} mv_i^2.$$

Here V is the speed of the gun + ball system after the ball sticks, U_s is the potential energy of spring + ball and f is the desired fraction. Solve for V in the first equation and substitute into the second; a factor v_i^2 then cancels and the remainder yields for f,

$$f = \frac{M}{m + M} \text{ Ans.}$$

10-26

Each particle imparts a momentum

$$p = 2\,mv = 2\,m\sqrt{2gh}$$

to the pan. If n particles strike the pan in a time t, the average force F exerted on the pan is

$$F = P/t = n(2\,m\sqrt{2gh})/t$$

$$F = (32)(2)(1/128 \text{ slug})\sqrt{2(32 \text{ ft/s}^2)(9 \text{ ft})}/(1 \text{ s}) = 12 \text{ lb Ans.}$$

10-28

Let the x-axis be vertical, positive downward with the origin at the top of the shaft. If the ball is dropped at t = 0,

$$x_b = \frac{1}{2} gt^2 , \quad x_e = h - vt,$$

where v is the speed of the elevator and h = 60 ft. If the ball and elevator collide at time t = t' we have

$$x_b(t') = x_e(t') \rightarrow h - vt' = \frac{1}{2} gt'^2 \rightarrow gt' = - v + \sqrt{v^2 + 2gh} ,$$

t'> 0. Relative to the elevator, the velocity of the ball is reversed by the collision: just before collision the relative velocity is $+(v + gt')$, and just after it is $-(v + gt')$. Thus the velocity of the ball relative to the shaft just after collision is $-(v + gt') - v = -(2v + gt')$. Therefore, the highest point x = H subsequently reached by the ball is given by

$$0^2 = (2v + gt')^2 + 2g[H - x_e(t')],$$

where $x_e(t') = h - vt'$. Putting this in and rearranging gives

$$- 4v^2 - 6v(gt') - (gt')^2 = 2g(H - h).$$

Finally, substitute for gt' from above and solve for H: one gets,

$$H = - 2(v/g)\sqrt{v^2 + 2gh} .$$

(a) Set v = + 6 ft/s; H = - 23 ft (i.e. above top of shaft) Ans.

(b) Put v = - 6 ft/s; H = + 23 ft (i.e. below top of shaft) Ans.

10-30

(a) In parenthesis we indicate the initial and final velocities for the specified mass in the collision under consideration. In the collision of the left (v_0, v') mass with the center $(0, u)$ mass

$$mv_0 + 0 = mv' + mu, \quad \frac{1}{2} mv_0^2 = \frac{1}{2} mv'^2 + \frac{1}{2} mu^2,$$

$$\rightarrow v' = 0, \ u = v_0.$$

Thus the left mass comes to rest. In the subsequent collision between the center (u, u') mass with the right (0, V) mass,

$$mu + 0 = mu' + MV, \quad \frac{1}{2}mu^2 = \frac{1}{2}mu'^2 + \frac{1}{2}MV^2,$$

$$\rightarrow V = 2v_0\frac{m}{m+M}, \quad u' = v_0\frac{m-M}{m+M}.$$

If $M \leqslant m$, $u' \geqslant 0$ and the center mass moves to the right with a velocity $u' < V$, so it never catches the right mass and, therefore, there are only two collisions.

(b) If $M > m$ the motion of the right mass is as above, but now $u' < 0$ and so the center mass moves to the left with a speed

$$-u' = v_0\frac{M-m}{M+m}.$$

This mass subsequently will collide with the stationary left mass and the two will exchange velocities.

10-31

In the collision between m and m':

$$mv = mv' + m'u, \qquad e(v - 0) = u - v';$$

in the collision between m' and M:

$$m'u = m'u' + MV, \qquad e'(u - 0) = V - u',$$

where $0 \leqslant e, e' \leqslant 1$ (the smaller value for a completely inelastic collision, the larger for an elastic collision). Eliminating v' from the first set of equations and u' from the second set gives, respectivelly,

$$u = \frac{mv}{m+m'}(1+e), \qquad V = \frac{m'u}{m'+M}(1+e').$$

Now eliminate u from these to obtain

$$V = \frac{m\,m'}{(m'+M)(m+m')}v(1+e)(1+e').$$

Therefore, the kinetic energy K of the mass M is

$$K = \frac{1}{2} MV^2 = \frac{1}{2} \frac{M m^2 m'^2}{(m' + M)^2 (m + m')^2} v^2 (1 + e)^2 (1 + e')^2.$$

Considered as a function of m', we find the maximum by the usual method:

$$\frac{dK}{dm'} = \frac{m' M m^2 (1 + e)^2 (1 + e')^2 v^2}{(m' + M)^3 (m + m')^3} (M m - m'^2),$$

which is zero for $m' = 0$, $m' \to \infty$ and, the desired value, $m' = \sqrt{M m}$.

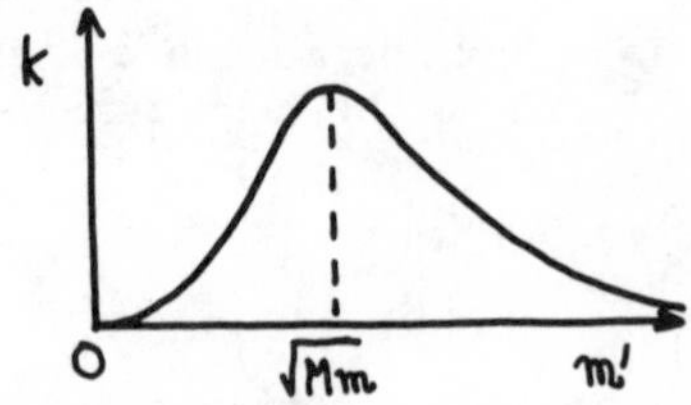

10-35

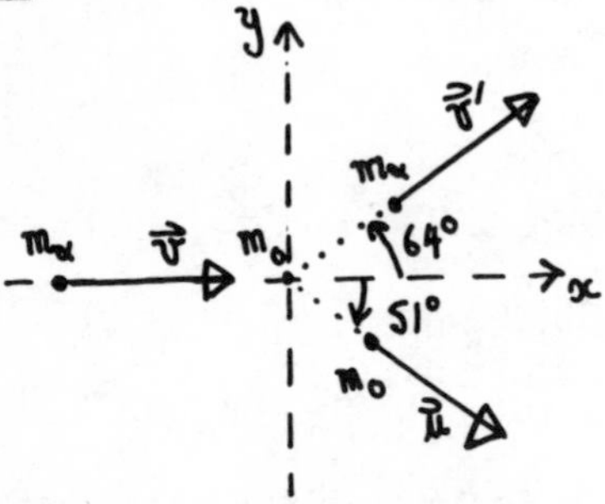

From conservation of the y-component of momentum,

$$m_\alpha v' \sin 64° = m_o u \sin 51°.$$

Since $m_o = 4 m_\alpha$ we have

$$\frac{v'}{u} = 4 \frac{\sin 51°}{\sin 64°} = 3.46 \text{ Ans.}$$

10-40

From momentum conservation,

$$mv - mv \cos\alpha = (2m)(v/2)\cos\beta,$$

$$mv \sin\alpha = (2m)(v/2)\sin\beta.$$

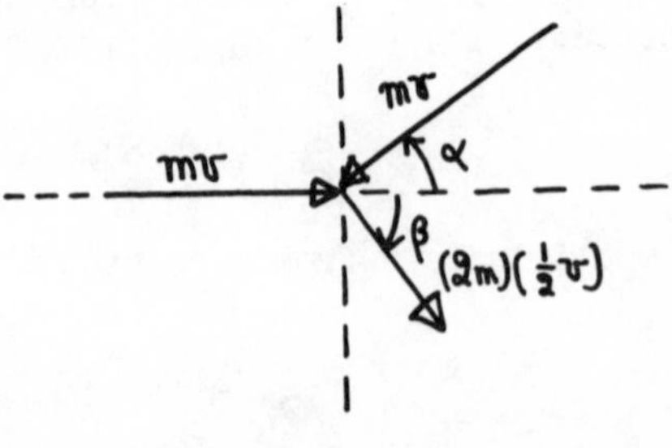

Solving for the angles we get

$$\alpha = \beta = \pi/3,$$

so that the angle between the initial velocities is $2\pi/3$ Ans.

10-41

Conservation of momentum and kinetic energy tell us that

$$m\,v = M\,u\cos\beta, \qquad (1)$$

$$m\,v' = M\,u\sin\beta, \qquad (2)$$

$$\frac{1}{2}mv^2 = \frac{1}{2}mv'^2 + \frac{1}{2}Mu^2. \qquad (3)$$

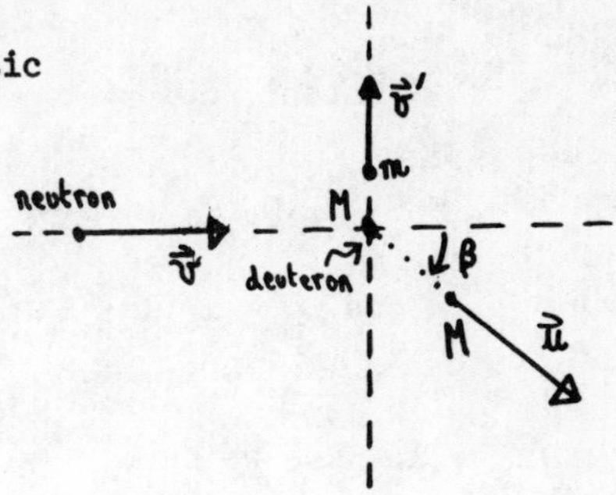

From (1) and (2),

$$M^2u^2 = m^2v^2 + m^2v'^2, \qquad (*)$$

and from (3),

$$m^2v'^2 = m^2v^2 - M\,mu^2.$$

Put this last into (*) and rearrange to get the kinetic energy of the deuteron:

$$\frac{1}{2}Mu^2 = \frac{m^2}{m + M}v^2.$$

But M = 2 m and therefore

$$\frac{1}{2}Mu^2 = \frac{m}{m + M}(mv^2) = \frac{1}{3}mv^2 = \frac{2}{3}\left(\frac{1}{2}mv^2\right),$$

which establishes the result quoted in the problem.

10-42

By conservation of momentum and kinetic energy,

$$m_1v_1 + 0 = m_1v_1'\cos\theta_1 + m_2v_2'\cos\theta_2,$$

$$0 = m_1v_1'\sin\theta_1 + m_2v_2'\sin\theta_2,$$

$$\frac{1}{2}m_1v_1^2 = \frac{1}{2}m_1v_1'^2 + \frac{1}{2}m_2v_2'^2.$$

Eliminating v_1' and v_2' yields

$$\tan\theta_1 = \sin2\theta_2/(\cos2\theta_2 - m_1/m_2).$$

(a) $m_1/m_2 > 1$. In this case,

$$d\tan\theta_1/d\theta_2 = 0 \rightarrow \tan\theta_m = -m_2(m_1^2 - m_2^2)^{-1/2}$$

since $2\theta_{2m} = \cos^{-1}(m_2/m_1)$. Hence

$$\cos^2\theta_m = 1/(1 + \tan^2\theta_m) = 1 - \frac{m_2^2}{m_1^2}.$$

(b) $m_1/m_2 = 1$. Here we have

$$\tan\theta_1 = (\sin 2\theta_2)/(\cos 2\theta_2 - 1) = \cot\theta_2 \rightarrow \theta_1 + \theta_2 = \pi/2.$$

(c) $m_1/m_2 < 1$. When $\cos 2\theta_2 = m_1/m_2$, $\tan\theta_1 \rightarrow \infty$; if $\sin 2\theta_2 < 0$, $\tan\theta_1 \rightarrow -\infty$. Thus all values of θ_1 are possible.

10-45

We know that

$$R_x = R_0 N\sigma/A.$$

Here $A = 1\ m^2$. Now 65 g of copper contain $N_0 = 6.02 \times 10^{23}$ atoms, so that 5×10^{-3} g must contain 4.63×10^{19} atoms by direct proportion. Hence,

$$(4.6 \times 10^{11}\ s^{-1}) = (1.1 \times 10^{18}\ /m^2\cdot s)(4.63 \times 10^{19})\sigma \times 10^{-28}\ m^2$$

$$\sigma = 90\ \text{b}\ \underline{\text{Ans.}}$$

10-49

(a) Directly from the information given,

$$\Delta(mc^2) = c^2(236 - 132 - 98)u = (6\ u)(1.66 \times 10^{-27}\ kg/u)\ c^2;$$

putting $c = 3 \times 10^8$ m/s gives,

$$\Delta(mc^2) = 5600\ \text{MeV},$$

since 1 eV = 1.6×10^{-19} J. Hence the energy lost is 5600 MeV - 192 MeV = 5400 MeV Ans.

(b) By conservation of momentum and the definition of Q,

$$m_A v_A = m_B v_B,$$

$$\frac{1}{2} m_A v_A^{\ 2} + \frac{1}{2} m_B v_B^{\ 2} - 0 = Q = 192 \text{ MeV} = 307 \times 10^{-13} \text{ J},$$

since the U^{236} nucleus was at rest. We have $m_A = 132$ u, $m_B = 98$ u and 1 u = 1.66×10^{-27} kg. With these we find

$$\left. \begin{aligned} v_A &= 1.09 \times 10^7 \text{ m/s}, \\ v_B = (m_A/m_B)v_A &= 1.47 \times 10^7 \text{ m/s} \end{aligned} \right\} \underline{\text{Ans.}}$$

(c) By straightforward calculation,

$$Q_A = \frac{1}{2} m_A v_A^{\ 2} = 81.7 \text{ MeV}, \quad Q_B = \frac{1}{2} m_B v_B^{\ 2} = 110 \text{ MeV } \underline{\text{Ans.}}$$

CHAPTER 11

11-3

(a) A wheel with 500 teeth also has 500 slots, so that the angular separation between adjacent slots is $2\pi/500$ rad. Thus the wheel rotates through an angle $\pi/250$ rad in the time taken for light to travel a distance 2L; this time t is 2L/c and therefore,

$$\omega t = \pi/250 \text{ rad}, \; t = 2L/c \;\rightarrow\; \omega = \pi\, c/(500\ L),$$

$$= \pi(3 \times 10^{8}\ \text{m/s})/(500)(500\ \text{m}) = 3770\ \text{rad/s}\ \underline{\text{Ans.}}$$

(b) The speed v at the rim is

$$v = r\omega = (5 \times 10^{-2}\ \text{m})(3770\ \text{rad/s}) = 190\ \text{m/s}\ \underline{\text{Ans.}}$$

11-5

By definition,

$$\bar{\alpha} = \frac{\omega(4) - \omega(2)}{4\ \text{s} - 2\ \text{s}}.$$

Since

$$\omega(t) = -6t + 3t^2, \;\rightarrow\; \omega(4) = 24\ \text{rad/s},\ \omega(2) = 0,$$

and therefore, by substitution,

$$\bar{\alpha} = 24/2 = 12\ \text{rad/s}^2\ \underline{\text{Ans.}}$$

11-8

This is essentially a problem in relative angular velocities. Since $\omega = 2\pi/T$, we have

$$\omega_S = \omega_E - \omega_P \;\rightarrow\; 2\pi/T_S = 2\pi/T_E - 2\pi/T_P,$$

$$\rightarrow\; 1/T_S = 1/T_E - 1/T_P\ \underline{\text{Ans.}}$$

11-14

Let ω_1 be the angular velocity at the start of the 4 s interval, and β the angle turned through in this time. Then,

$$\beta = \frac{1}{2}\alpha t^2 + \omega_1 t + \beta_0 \rightarrow 120 \text{ rad} = \frac{1}{2}(3 \text{ rad/s}^2)(4 \text{ s})^2 + \omega_1(4 \text{ s}),$$
$$\rightarrow \omega_1 = 24 \text{ rad/s}.$$

Now if T = the time the wheel had been rotating before the start of the 4 s interval, and the wheel started from rest ($\omega_0 = 0$), we must have

$$\omega_1 = \alpha T + \omega_0 \rightarrow 24 \text{ rad/s} = (3 \text{ rad/s}^2)T + 0,$$
$$T = 8.0 \text{ s} \ \underline{\text{Ans.}}$$

11-16

Note that 40 rev = 80π rad. Considering the motion in reverse, we have

(a)

$$\left.\begin{aligned} 1.5 \text{ rad/s} &= \alpha t \\ 80\pi \text{ rad} &= \frac{1}{2}\alpha t^2 \end{aligned}\right\} \quad 80\pi = \frac{1}{2}(1.5/t)t^2 \rightarrow t = 335 \text{ s} \ \underline{\text{Ans.}}$$

(b)

$$\alpha = \omega/t = (1.5 \text{ rad/s})/(335 \text{ s}) = -4.5 \times 10^{-3} \text{ rad/s}^2 \ \underline{\text{Ans.}}$$

(c) Still considering the motion in reverse, find how long it takes to complete 20 rev when speeding up:

$$40\pi \text{ rad} = \frac{1}{2}(4.5 \times 10^{-3} \text{ rad/s}^2)\, t^2,$$

$$t = 236 \text{ s}.$$

It follows that the time to complete 20 rev when slowing down is

$$340 - 236 = 104 \text{ s} \ \underline{\text{Ans.}}$$

11-19

If the belt does not slip, the linear velocities at the rims of the wheels are the same at any time; to wit,

$$r_A\omega_A = r_C\omega_C.$$

Differentiating with respect to time,

$$\alpha_C = (r_A/r_C)\alpha_A.$$

Now $\omega_C = \alpha_C t + \omega_{OC}$ and $\omega_{OC} = 0$. Hence,

$$\omega_C = (r_A/r_C)\alpha_A t.$$

Since ω_C = 100 rpm corresponds to (100)(2π)/(60) rad/s,

$$200\pi/60 \text{ rad/s} = (10 \text{ cm}/25 \text{ cm})(\pi/2 \text{ rad/s}^2)\ t,$$
$$t = 50/3 \text{ s} \quad \underline{\text{Ans.}}$$

11-25

We know that

$$\omega_0 = 150 \text{ rev/min} = 150(2\pi)/60 = 15.7 \text{ rad/s},$$
$$T = 2.2 \text{ h} = 7920 \text{ s}.$$

(a) Since the final angular velocity is zero,

$$\alpha = -\omega_0/T = -(15.7 \text{ rad/s})/(7920 \text{ s}) = -0.002 \text{ rad/s}^2 \quad \underline{\text{Ans.}}$$

(b) If the angle turned through is β,

$$\beta = \tfrac{1}{2}(0.002 \text{ rad/s}^2)(7920 \text{ s})^2 = 6.27 \times 10^4 \text{ rad},$$

treating the motion in reverse. Since 1 rev = 2π rad,

$$\text{no. rev.} = \beta/2\pi = 10^4 \text{ rev} \quad \underline{\text{Ans.}}$$

(c) The tangential acceleration is

$$a_T = \alpha\, r = (-0.002 \text{ rad/s}^2)(0.50 \text{ m}) \rightarrow \alpha_T = -1.0 \text{ mm/s}^2.$$

(d) The total linear acceleration a is given by $a^2 = a_T{}^2 + a_R{}^2$. In (c) we found a_T. As for a_R,

$$a_R = \omega^2 r = (0.50 \text{ m})(150\ \pi/60)^2 = 30.84 \text{ m/s}^2.$$

Evidently $a_R \gg a_T$. Thus we find

$$a \approx a_R = 31 \text{ m/s}^2 \ \underline{\text{Ans.}}$$

<u>11-28</u>

Converting the angular speed to rad/s,

$$\omega = (33\ \tfrac{1}{3})(2\pi)/(60) = 3.49 \text{ rad/s}.$$

(a) The velocity is

$$v_T = r\omega = (12 \text{ cm})(3.49 \text{ rad/s}) = 42 \text{ cm/s } \underline{\text{Ans}},$$

for the tangential component and

$$v_R = 1.6 \text{ cm/s, outward } \underline{\text{Ans}},$$

for the radial.

(b) We give the radial and tangential components:

$$a_R = r\omega^2 = (12 \text{ cm})(3.49 \text{ rad/s})^2 = 150 \text{ cm/s}^2, \text{ inward } \underline{\text{Ans}};$$

$$a_T = 2\,\omega\frac{dr}{dt} = 2(3.49 \text{ rad/s})(1.6 \text{ cm/s}) = 11 \text{ cm/s}^2 \ \underline{\text{Ans.}}$$

(c) Let the coefficient be μ. Since $g = 980 \text{ cm/s}^2$,

$$\mu mg = ma_R = m(16 \text{ cm})(3.49 \text{ rad/s})^2,$$

$$\rightarrow \mu = 0.20 \ \underline{\text{Ans.}}$$

12-8

We have, by straightforward calculations:

(a)

$$I = \sum m_i r_i^2 = mL^2 + m(2L)^2 + m(3L)^2 = 14\ m\ L^2 \ \underline{\text{Ans}};$$

(b)

$$L_m = I_m \omega = m(2\ L)^2 \omega = 4\ m\ L^2 \omega \ \underline{\text{Ans}};$$

(c)

$$L_T = I_T \omega = 14\ m\ L^2 \omega \ \underline{\text{Ans}}.$$

12-13

We can treat the three rods, placed, as they are, end to end, as one single rod of length 3L and mass 3M.

(a) If I is the total rotational inertia,

$$I = I_{masses} + I_{rods} = 14\ m\ L^2 + \frac{1}{3}(3M)(3L)^2 = 14\ mL^2 + 9ML^2 \ \underline{\text{Ans}}.$$

(b) It follows from (a) that the rotational kinetic energy R is

$$R = \frac{1}{2}\ I\omega^2 = \frac{1}{2}(14\ mL^2 + 9\ ML^2)\omega^2 = (7\ m + \frac{9}{2}\ M)L^2\omega^2 \ \underline{\text{Ans}}.$$

12-16

(a) If we orient the x,y-axes as shown, then

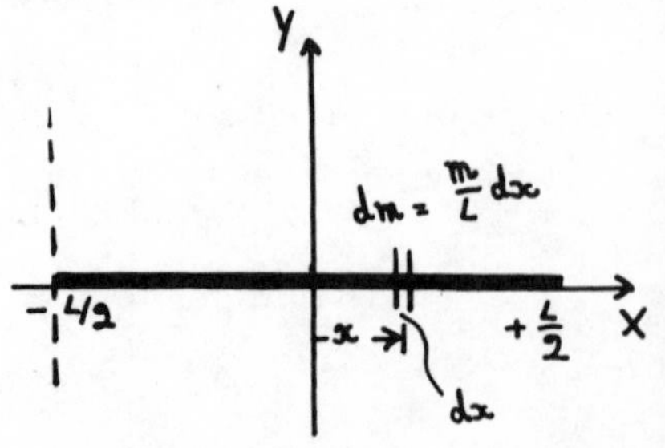

$$I = \int x^2 dm = \int x^2 \frac{m}{L}\ dx$$

$$= \frac{m}{L} \int_{-L/2}^{+L/2} x^2\ dx = \frac{1}{12}\ mL^2 \ \underline{\text{Ans}}.$$

(b) The rotational inertia calculated in (a) is calculated about an axis through the center of mass. Hence, by the parallel- axis theorem, the rotational inertia about a parallel axis through one end is

$$I_e = I_{cm} + mh^2 = \frac{1}{12} mL^2 + m(\frac{L}{2})^2 = \frac{1}{3} mL^2 \ \underline{\text{Ans.}}$$

12-20

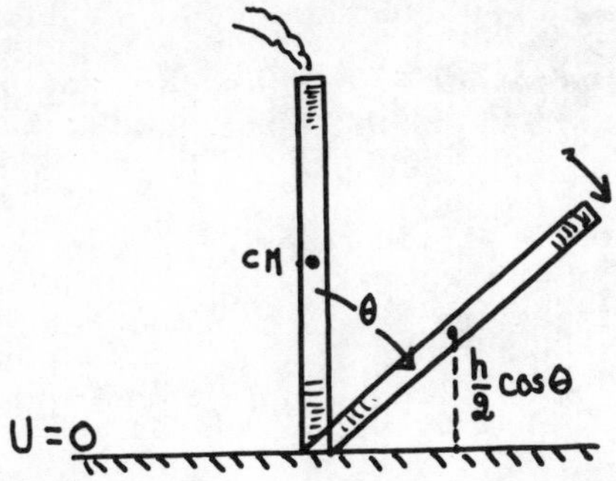

(a) The radial acceleration is $a_R = h\,\omega^2$. By energy conservation,

$$mg\,\frac{h}{2} = \frac{1}{2} I\omega^2 + mg\,\frac{h}{2}\cos\theta,$$

where $I = \frac{1}{3} mh^2$, since the chimney is, in effect, rotating about an axis through its base. Inserting the expression for I yields

$$mgh(1 - \cos\theta) = \frac{1}{3} mh^2\omega^2,$$

and therefore

$$a_R = h\omega^2 = 3g(1 - \cos\theta) \ \underline{\text{Ans.}}$$

(b) The tangential acceleration is

$$a_T = \frac{dv}{dt} = \frac{d}{dt}(h\omega) = h\,\alpha.$$

Using the result from (a),

$$\alpha = \frac{d\omega}{dt} = \frac{1}{2}\frac{1}{\omega}\left(\frac{3g}{h}\sin\theta\right)\frac{d\theta}{dt} = \frac{3g}{2h}\sin\theta,$$

since $\frac{d\theta}{dt} = \omega$. Hence the tangential acceleration is

$$a_T = h\,\alpha = \frac{3g}{2}\sin\theta \ \underline{\text{Ans.}}$$

(c) Clearly

$$a = \sqrt{a_R^2 + a_T^2} = \frac{3g}{2}\sqrt{(1 - \cos\theta)(5 - 3\cos\theta)} > g$$

for θ close to $\pi/2$; indeed, $a > g$ for $\theta > 55\frac{1}{2}^\circ$. Thus the answer is yes.

(d) As the chimney tips over, the weight of the upper parts acts transverse to the chimney. Chimneys standing upright are not subjected to such transverse forces and therefore are not specifically designed to withstand them.

12-26

(a) By definition,

$$\bar{\tau} = \Delta L/\Delta t = (2 - 3)(\text{kg}\cdot\text{m}^2/\text{s})/(1.5\ \text{s}) = -\ 0.67\ \text{N}\cdot\text{m}\ \underline{\text{Ans.}}$$

(b) Since $\tau = I\alpha$,

$$\alpha = (-\ 0.67\ \text{N}\cdot\text{m})/(0.125\ \text{kg}\cdot\text{m}^2) = -\ 5.36\ \text{rad/s}^2.$$

The initial and final angular velocities are

$$\omega_i = L_i/I = (3)/(0.125) = 24\ \text{rad/s},\ \omega_f = L_f/I = (2)/(0.125) = 16/\text{s}.$$

Since $\omega_f = \alpha t + \omega_i$,

$$16\ \text{rad/s} = (-\ 5.36\ \text{rad/s}^2)t + 24\ \text{rad/s} \rightarrow t = 1.5\ \text{s}.$$

Thus the angle β turned through in this time is

$$\beta = \tfrac{1}{2}(-\ 5.36\ \text{rad/s}^2)(1.5\ \text{s})^2 + (24\ \text{rad/s})(1.5\ \text{s}) = 30\ \text{rad},$$

and the number of revolutions made is $\beta/2\pi = 4.8$ Ans.

(c) By the work-energy theorem,

$$W = \Delta K = K_f - K_i = \frac{1}{2}I(\omega_f^2 - \omega_i^2) = \tfrac{1}{2}(0.125)(256 - 576)\ \text{J}$$

$$W = -\ 20\ \text{J}\ \underline{\text{Ans.}}$$

(d) The power supplied by the flywheel is $P = 20\ \text{J}/1.5\ \text{s} = 13\ \text{W}$ Ans.

12-27

Let the masses be m_1, m_2 $(m_2 > m_1)$; W, R, M the weight, radius and mass of the pulley, the rotational inertia of which is I about the axis of rotation. The acceleration of the masses is a, and the

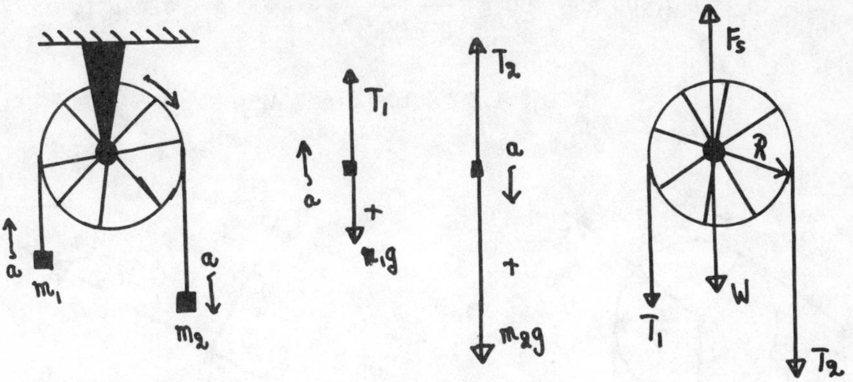

angular acceleration of the pulley α. The pulley is supported by a force F_s. We draw free-body diagrams of all object. For the two masses,

$$\left.\begin{aligned} m_1g - T_1 &= -m_1a \\ m_2g - T_2 &= m_2a \end{aligned}\right\} \rightarrow a = \frac{(m_2 - m_1)g + (T_1 - T_2)}{m_1 + m_2}.$$

For the pulley $\tau = I\alpha$, where $\alpha = a/R$. Now clearly $F_s = T_1 + T_2 + W$, but neither $\vec{F}_s$ nor $\vec{W}$ exert any torque about the axis of rotation of the pulley. Hence we have

$$(m_1 + m_2)a = (m_2 - m_1)g - Ia/R^2 \rightarrow I = R^2\left[(m_2 - m_1)\frac{g}{a} - (m_1 + m_2)\right],$$

since

$$(T_2 - T_1)R = I\alpha \rightarrow T_2 - T_1 = Ia/R^2.$$

As m_2 is observed to fall from rest a distance of 75 cm in 5 s,

$$a = 2(75\ \text{cm})/(5\ \text{s})^2 = 6\ \text{cm/s}^2.$$

Therefore we have finally,

$$I = (5\ \text{cm})^2\left[(500\ \text{g} - 460\ \text{g})\frac{980\ \text{cm/s}^2}{6\ \text{cm/s}^2} - (500\ \text{g} + 460\ \text{g})\right],$$

$$I = 1.39 \times 10^5\ \text{g}\cdot\text{cm}^2\ \underline{\text{Ans.}}$$

12-29

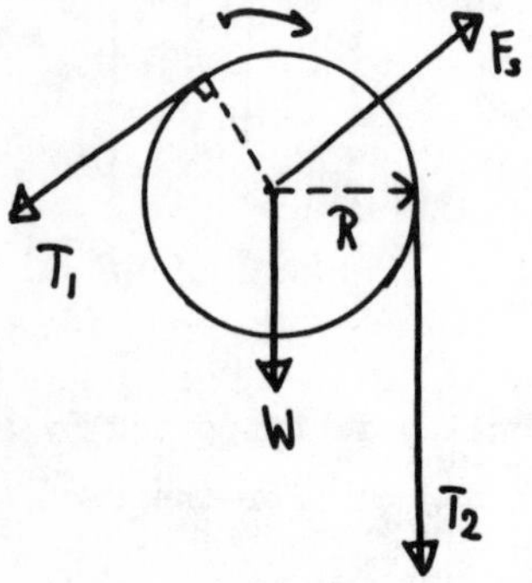

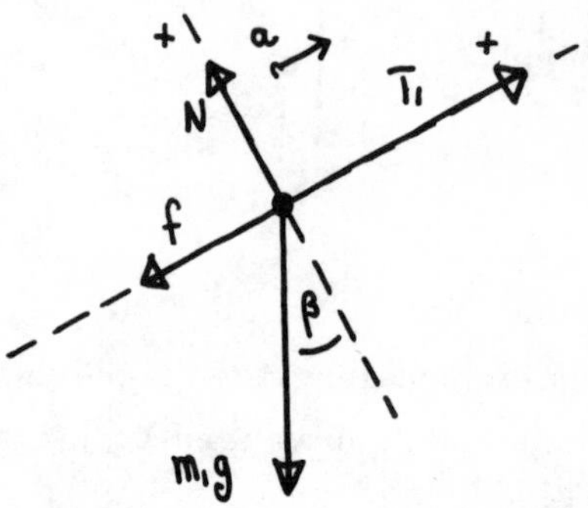

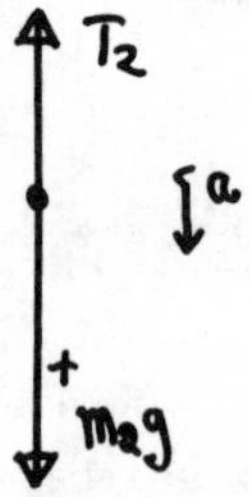

We use the same notation as in problem 12-27, except that the force of friction is $f = \mu N$. We assume that m_1 is moving and accelerating up the plane. The equations of motion for m_1 and m_2 are

$$T_1 - m_1 g \sin\beta - f = m_1 a,$$
$$N - m_1 g \cos\beta = 0,$$
$$f = \mu N;$$

$$m_2 g - T_2 = m_2 a.$$

These give

$$(m_1 + m_2)a = m_2 g - m_1 g(\sin\beta + \mu\cos\beta) - (T_2 - T_1).$$

The rotational equation for the pulley is

$$(T_2 - T_1)R = I\alpha = Ia/R \rightarrow T_2 - T_1 = Ia/R^2.$$

But $I = \frac{1}{2} MR^2$; thus

$$T_2 - T_1 = \frac{1}{2} Ma.$$

Substituting this into the equation for a, given at the bottom of of the previous page, yields for us,

(a) $$a = g \frac{m_2 - m_1(\sin\beta + \mu\cos\beta)}{m_1 + m_2 + M/2},$$

$$a = (32 \text{ ft/s}^2) \frac{(0.5625 \text{ slug}) - (0.1875 \text{ slug})(.5 + .0866)}{(0.5625 + 0.1875 + 0.03125)\text{slug}},$$

$$a = 0.58\ g = 18.53 \text{ ft/s}^2 \ \underline{\text{Ans.}}$$

(b) We may find T_2 from the equation of motion for m_2:

$$T_2 = m_2 g(1 - \frac{a}{g}) = (18 \text{ lb})(1 - 0.58) = 7.56 \text{ lb} \ \underline{\text{Ans}},$$

and T_1 from the equation for the pulley:

$$T_1 = T_2 - \frac{1}{2} Ma = 7.56 \text{ lb} - \frac{1}{2}(0.0625 \text{ slug})(18.53 \text{ ft/s}^2),$$

$$T_1 = 6.98 \text{ lb} \ \underline{\text{Ans.}}$$

<u>12-33</u>

We know that $\vec{v}_A \perp \overline{AP}$, $\vec{v}_B \perp \overline{BP}$. Since $\vec{v}_A$ and $\vec{v}_B$ are along the wall and floor respectively, we locate P as shown in the figure: taking the intersection of lines through A and B perpendicular to the wall and floor.

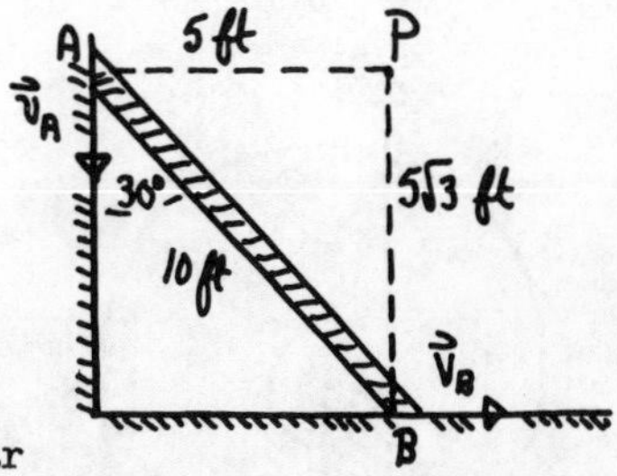

12-38

(a) With the acceleration zero,

$$T - Mg = 0 \rightarrow T = Mg \ \underline{\text{Ans.}}$$

(b) By the work-energy theorem,

$$W = \frac{1}{2} I\omega^2 - 0 = \frac{1}{2}\left(\frac{1}{2} MR^2\right)\omega^2 = \frac{1}{4} MR^2\omega^2 \ \underline{\text{Ans.}}$$

(c) If β is the angle turned through,

$$W = \tau\beta = (T\,R)(L/R) = T\,L = Mg\,L = \frac{1}{4} MR^2\omega^2,$$

by (b). Here L is the length of string unwound. Thus,

$$L = R^2\omega^2/4\,g \ \underline{\text{Ans.}}$$

12-41

From an example worked in the text, we know that the acceleration of the center of mass of a circular cylinder rolling down an inclined plane is

$$a = \frac{2}{3} g \sin\theta,$$

independent of the radius of the cylinder. Thus, if the wound tape remains circular, the time for the tape to unwind, and hence for the center of mass to move a distance L, the length of the tape, is given by

$$L = \frac{1}{2}\left(\frac{2}{3} g \sin\theta\right)T^2 \rightarrow T = \sqrt{\frac{3L}{g \sin\theta}} \ \underline{\text{Ans.}}$$

12-43

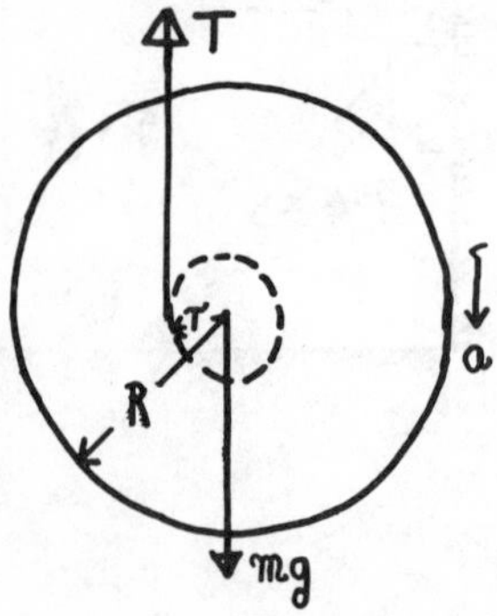

The equations of motion are,

$$T - mg = -\,ma,$$

$$T\,r = I\,\alpha = I\,\frac{a}{r}.$$

Note that the acceleration is directed downward during both descent and ascent: at the bottom point the velocity is reversed, giving the yo-yo an initial upward velocity. We put $I = \frac{1}{2} mR^2$, ignoring the contribution of the shaft which should be small if $r \ll R$.

(a) Solving the equations for the tension we get,

$$T = \frac{mgR^2}{R^2 + 2r^2} \quad \text{(up or down motion) } \underline{\text{Ans.}}$$

(b) Let t be the desired time. If the length of the string is L + R, the center of the yo-yo will decend a distance L. Therefore, since

$$t = 2\sqrt{\frac{2\,L}{a}},$$

and, from the equations of motion,

$$a = g\,\frac{1}{1 + R^2/2r^2},$$

we obtain

$$t = 2\sqrt{\frac{2\,L}{g}(1 + R^2/2r^2)} \quad \underline{\text{Ans.}}$$

<u>12-45</u>

Apparently the pulley is to be considered massless. With $\vec{f}$ being the force of friction ($f \neq \mu N$, $\vec{N}$ not shown **since it is of no** import), the equations of motion are,

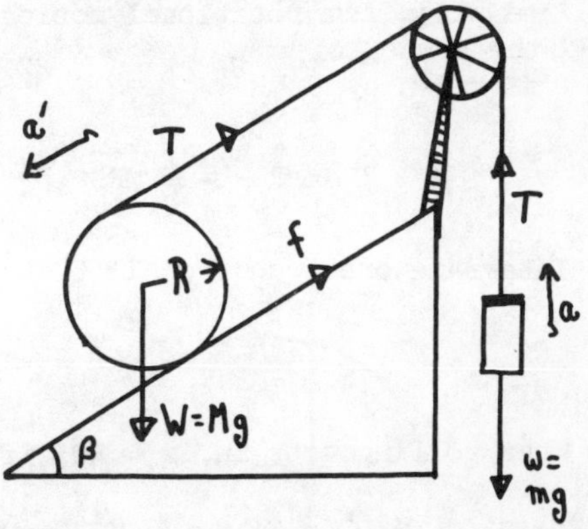

$$T - mg = ma,$$

$$T + f - Mg\sin\beta = -Ma',$$

$$(f - T)R = I\alpha = \frac{1}{2}MRa',$$

since $a' = \alpha R$. The tape winds up around the cylinder as it rolls down the incline, and therefore

$$a = a' + \alpha R = 2\,a'.$$

Eliminating f and solving simultaneously gives:

(a) $$a' = g\,\frac{W \sin\beta - 2w}{(3/2)W + 4w} = g/23 = 1.4 \text{ ft/s}^2 \ \underline{\text{Ans}},$$

(b) $$T = m(g + a) = w(1 + 2\,\frac{a'}{g}) = \frac{25}{23}\,w = 11 \text{ lb } \underline{\text{Ans}},$$

since $W = 50$ lb, $w = 10$ lb and $\beta = 30°$. These results are not dependent on the radius R of the cylinder.

<u>12-46</u>

Suppose the ball is struck at $x = t = \theta = 0$. We choose x increasing to the left and positive rotations counterclockwise. The impulse is to the right. While the ball is slipping, the equation for translational motion is

$$M\ddot{x} = \mu N = \mu Mg \rightarrow \ddot{x} = \mu g.$$

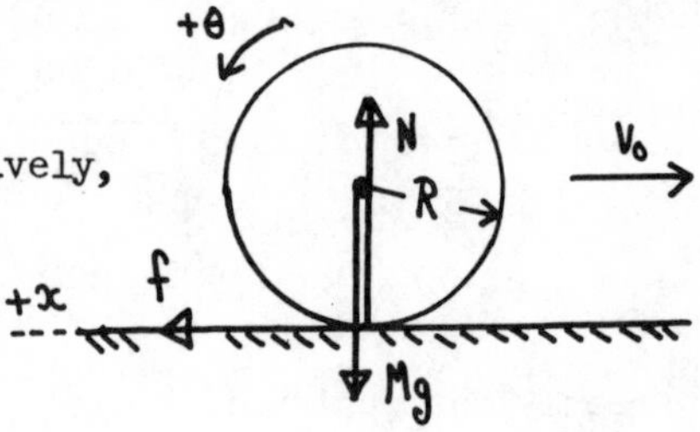

Integrating twice we get, successively,

$$\dot{x} = \mu gt - v_0, \quad x = \tfrac{1}{2}\mu gt^2 - v_0 t.$$

Similarly, for rotational motion,

$$fR = I\alpha = -\frac{2}{5}\,MR^2\ddot{\theta},$$

$$\mu mgR = -\frac{2}{5}\,MR^2\ddot{\theta} \rightarrow \ddot{\theta} = -\frac{5}{2}\,\mu g/R.$$

Integrate once, and recall that $\theta(0) = 0$ to obtain

$$R\dot{\theta} = -\frac{5}{2}\,\mu gt.$$

When rolling sets in, $\dot{x} = R\dot{\theta}$; if this happens at time $t = t'$, then

$$\mu gt' - v_0 = -\frac{5}{2}\,\mu gt' \rightarrow t' = \frac{2}{7}\,v_0/\mu g.$$

The distance travelled in this time is $-\,x(t')$. Putting the above value of t' into the equation for x(t) gives for the distance, $-\,x(t') = \frac{12}{49}\,v_0^{\,2}/\mu g$ <u>Ans</u>.

CHAPTER 13

13-4

We know from the text that the precession frequency ω_p is

$$\omega_p = MgR/L,$$

where M is the total mass of the top (or gyroscope), R the distance from support to the center of mass, and L is the spin angular momentum. Clearly, $M = m + m'$, m being the mass of the disc (the mass of the axle is neglected). Adding m' to the end of the axle shifts the center of mass from the center of the axle to a point farther out, a distance R from the support, given by

$$(m + m')R = mb + m'(2b) \rightarrow R = \frac{m + 2m'}{m + m'} b;$$

here, the length of the axle is 2b. Since m' is situated on the axle itself, it does not contribute to the rotational inertia of the gyroscope about the axle. Hence

$$L = I\omega = \frac{1}{2} ma^2\omega,$$

a the radius of the disc. Substituting these results into the formula for the precession frequency we get

$$\omega_p = (1 + 2\frac{m'}{m})(2gb/\omega a^2).$$

The second factor is the precession frequency without m': from problem 13-3 this is 43 rev/min. Thus, for the present problem,

$$\omega_p = (1 + 2\,r)43 \text{ rev/min } \underline{\text{Ans.}}$$

13-12

Let the linear impulse be $J = 3$ lb·s. The stick acquires a speed v determined from

$$J = mv - 0 \rightarrow v = \frac{J}{m} = \frac{3\ \text{lb}\cdot\text{s}}{0.3\ \text{slug}} = 10\ \text{ft/s}\ \underline{\text{Ans}},$$

in the direction of the impulse. Consider rotations about the center of mass. The rotational inertia of the stick about a perpendicular axis through the center of mass is

$$I = \frac{1}{12}\,md^2 = \frac{1}{12}(0.3\ \text{slug})(4\ \text{ft})^2 = 0.4\ \text{slug}\cdot\text{ft}^2.$$

Since the force strikes at a right-angle to the stick, the angular impulse is LJ and this equals the change in angular momentum; thus the stick acquires an angular velocity ω about the center of mass given by,

$$LJ = I\omega \rightarrow \omega = LJ/I = (1.5\ \text{ft})(3\ \text{lb}\cdot\text{s})/(0.4\ \text{slug}\cdot\text{ft}^2),$$

$$= 11\ \text{rad/s}\ \underline{\text{Ans}}.$$

13-17

Let $\vec{F}(t)$ be the force exerted by the disc on the cylinder as the disc slips by; from Newton's third law, the cylinder exerts a force $-\vec{F}(t)$ on the disc. If we integrate over the time the disc slips, and apply the equation for angular impulse to the cylinder, and linear impulse to the disc we shall have,

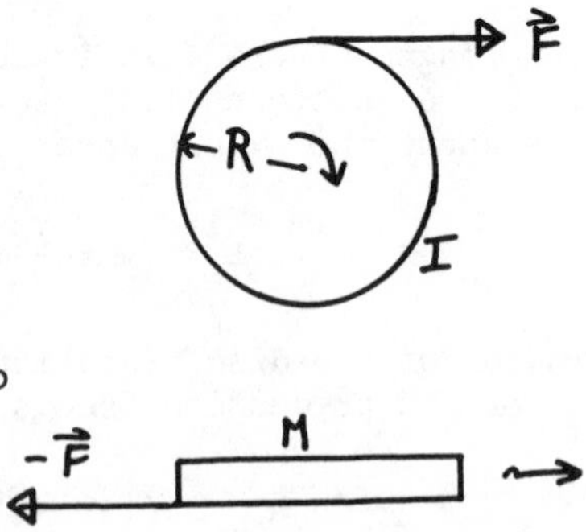

$$R\int F(t)\,dt = I\omega, \qquad -\int F(t)\,dt = M(v_2 - v_1),$$

ω being the final angular velocity of the cylinder. When slipping ceases we must have $v_2 = R\omega$. Invoking this, and eliminating $\int F\,dt$ from the two equations we solve for v_2:

$$M(v_1 - v_2) = I\,\frac{\omega}{R} = \frac{I}{R}\,(v_2/R),$$

$$v_2 = \frac{M\,v_1}{M + I/R^2} = \frac{v_1}{1 + I/MR^2} \quad \underline{\text{Ans.}}$$

13-19

Let F' be the average reaction force, and v_0, ω_0 the velocity of the center of mass and angular velocity about the suspension, immediately after impact. The impulse of the striking blow is F Δt, so that

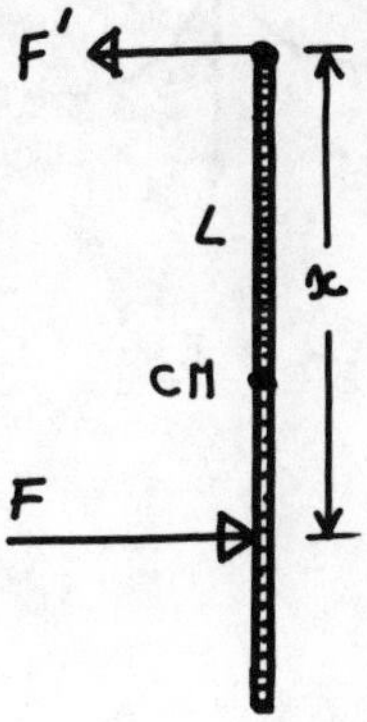

$$(F - F')\Delta t = \Delta(mv) = mv_0.$$

The angular impulse, calculated about the point of suspension, is (Fx)Δt so we also have

$$(F\,x)\Delta t = \Delta(I\omega) = I\omega_0.$$

But $v_0 = L\omega_0$; with this we may eliminate v_0 and ω_0 from the set of two equations and solve for F':

$$F' = \frac{F(I/mL - x)}{I/mL}.$$

For F' = 0, x = I/mL. Since $I = (4/3)mL^2$ about the point of suspension, the needed x is x = 4L/3 Ans.

13-20

(a) If the friction forces between the wheels are F_1 and F_2, Newton's third law indicates that $F_1 = F_2 = F$, say. Let ω_1' be the angular velocity of the first wheel after slipping ceases. Then the equation of angular impulse, applied to each cylinder, yields

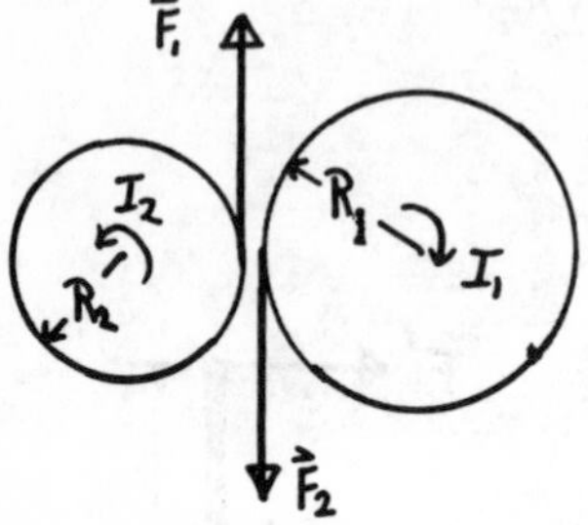

$$R_2 \int F\, dt = I_2(\omega_2 - 0),$$

$$- R_1 \int F\, dt = I_1(\omega_1' - \omega_0).$$

When slipping ceases $R_1\omega_1' = R_2\omega_2$. Using this, and eliminating the impulse gives us

$$I_2\omega_2 = R_2 \frac{I_1}{R_1}(\omega_0 - \omega_1') = \frac{R_2}{R_1} I_1 \left(\omega_0 - \frac{R_2\omega_2}{R_1}\right),$$

$$\omega_2 = \frac{\omega_0}{\frac{R_1 I_2}{R_2 I_1} + \frac{R_2}{R_1}} \quad \underline{\text{Ans.}}$$

(b) The total angular momentum is not conserved since torques must be applied to keep the wheels from climbing around one another.

13-21

The force of friction is $\vec{f}$. Positive directions of rotation and translation are indicated on the diagram. The impulse and angular impulse equations are

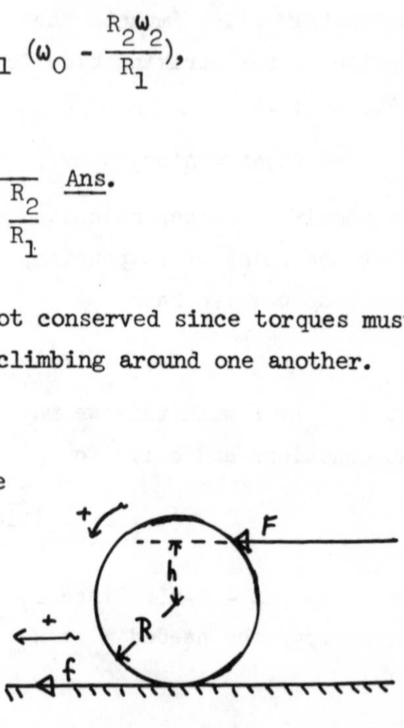

$$\int F\, dt = mv_0,$$

$$h \int F\, dt = I\omega_0,$$

where ω_0 is the initial angular velocity. Solving for this quantity,

$$\omega_0 = h\, m\, v_0/I.$$

The force of friction exerts a torque, and also accelerates the the ball. Hence we have,

$$fR = -I\alpha = -\frac{2}{5}mR^2\frac{d\omega}{dt} \rightarrow ft = -\frac{2}{5}mR(\omega - \omega_0),$$

$$ft = -\frac{2}{5}mR(\omega - hmv_0/R),$$

using the expression for ω_0 derived first. In addition,

$$f = m\frac{dv}{dt} \rightarrow v = \frac{f}{m}t + v_0.$$

Thus,

$$ft = m(v - v_0) = -\frac{2}{5}mR(\omega - hmv_0/I).$$

When rolling sets in $v = R\omega = \frac{9}{7}v_0$, the last by supposition. Substituting this for v results in

$$\frac{2}{7}mv_0 = -\frac{2}{5}mR\left[\frac{9v_0}{7R} - \frac{hmv_0}{\frac{2}{5}mR^2}\right],$$

$$h = \frac{4}{5}R \text{ } \underline{\text{Ans.}}$$

13-26

(a) The angular momentum about a vertical axis is conserved, so that

$$I_i\omega_i = I_f\omega_f.$$

The initial angular momentum is due only to the wheel, but the entire system participates in the motion after the wheel has been stopped. Thus,

$$(8.36 \text{ lb}/32 \text{ ft/s}^2)(1.14 \text{ ft})^2(57.7 \text{ rad/s}) = (1.54 \text{ slug}\cdot\text{ft}^2)\omega_f,$$

$$\omega_f = 12.6 \text{ rad/s, clockwise from above } \underline{\text{Ans.}}$$

(b) Although friction acts more slowly than simply grasping hold of the rim, the torques are still internal and angular momentum is conserved. The final motion is the same as in (a).

13-30

The angular momentum of the system child + merry-go-round about the axis of rotation of the merry-go-round is conserved. Since the merry-go-round is still before the child arrives we have, if m and v are the mass and speed of the child before jumping on, and $I = Mk^2$ is the rotational inertia of the merry-go round,

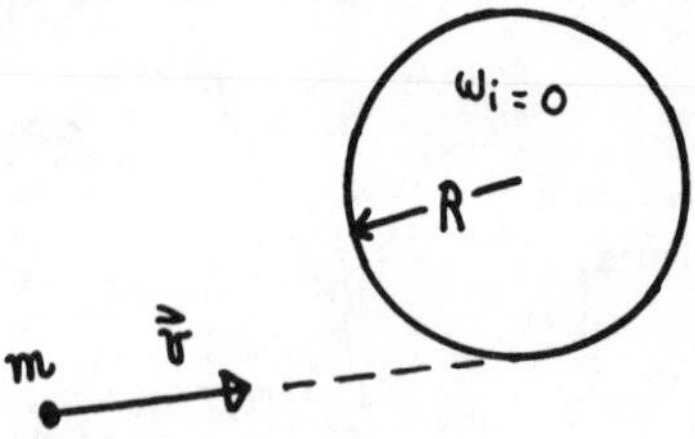

'before'

$$m\,v\,R = (I + mR^2)\omega = (Mk^2 + mR^2)\omega,$$

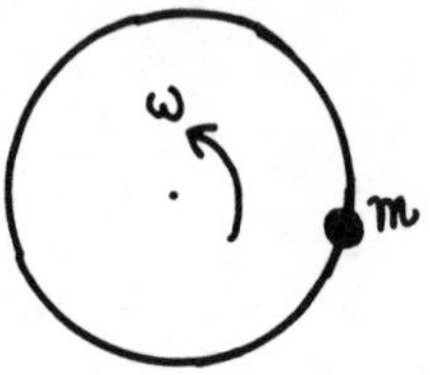

after

since the rotational inertia of the child, treated as a point mass, is mR^2 once she is on the merry-go-round. Putting in the numbers,

$$\omega = \frac{(3\text{ slug})(10\text{ ft/s})(4\text{ ft})}{(12\text{ slug})(3\text{ ft})^2 + (3\text{ slug})(4\text{ ft})^2} = 0.77\text{ rad/s } \underline{\text{Ans.}}$$

13-32

(a) We use conservation of angular momentum of the system (lazy-susan + cockroach). Taking account of directions, and assuming the cockroach to be a point mass so that its rotational inertia can be written mr^2, we get

$$I\omega_0 - mvR = (I + mR^2)\omega \rightarrow \omega = \frac{I\omega_0 - mvR}{I + mR^2} \;\; \underline{\text{Ans.}}$$

(b) Kinetic energy is not conserved since friction must be present for the cockroach to be able to stop.

13-35

(a) The total angular momentum is zero initially and must remain zero: thus,

$$MVR = mvR \rightarrow MR^2\dot{\theta} = mR^2\dot{\beta}.$$

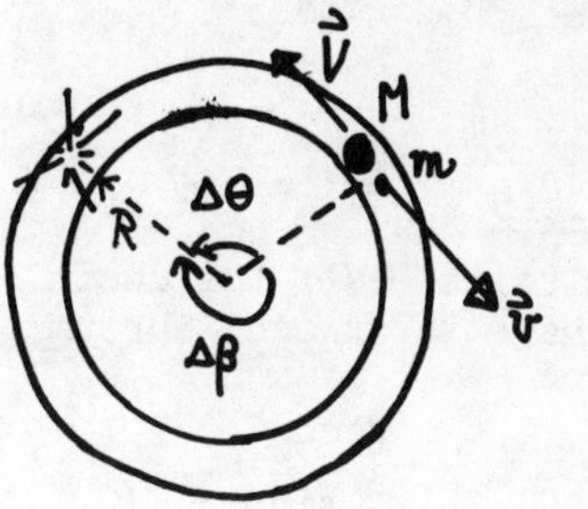

Hence

$$M\dot{\theta} = m\dot{\beta} \rightarrow M\Delta\theta = m\Delta\beta.$$

Now at collision, $\Delta\theta + \Delta\beta = 2\pi$ so that

$$M\Delta\theta = m(2\pi - \Delta\theta) \rightarrow \Delta\theta = \frac{2\pi m}{m + M} \ \underline{\text{Ans.}}$$

(b) By conservation of energy

$$\frac{1}{2} MV^2 + \frac{1}{2} mv^2 = U_0 \rightarrow \frac{1}{2} MR^2\dot{\theta}^2 + \frac{1}{2} mR^2\dot{\beta}^2 = U_0.$$

But from (a)

$$\dot{\beta} = M\dot{\theta}/m,$$

and therefore, since $\theta(0) = 0$,

$$\dot{\theta} = \sqrt{2U_0 m/MR^2(m + M)} \rightarrow \theta = \sqrt{2U_0 m/MR^2(m + M)}\ t.$$

Let the time of collision be $t = t_c$; $\theta(t_c) = \Delta\theta = 2\pi m/(m + M)$ from (a). Substituting this,

$$2\pi m/(m + M) = \sqrt{2U_0 m/MR^2(m + M)}\ t_c \rightarrow t_c = \sqrt{\frac{2\pi^2 mMR^2}{(m + M)U_0}} \ \underline{\text{Ans.}}$$

(c) Since the momentum is zero the particle velocities simply reverse on the initial collision and the particles will next collide at the original starting position.

14-5

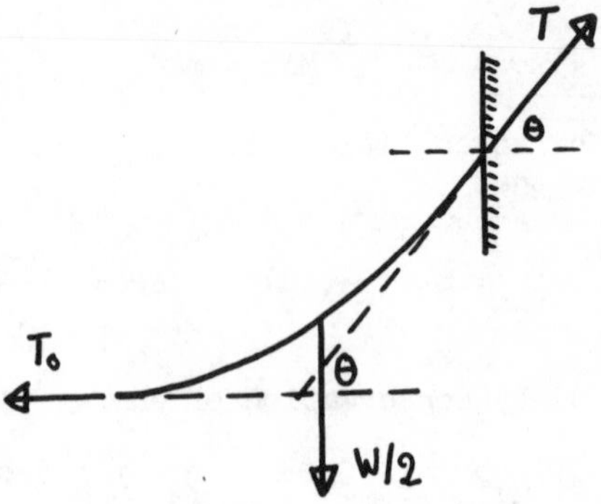

Isolate half the chain. Since the half is in equilibrium,

$$T\cos\theta = T_0,$$
$$T\sin\theta = W/2.$$

Solving for T_0, T gives

(a)

$$T = \frac{W}{2\sin\theta}\text{, tangent to chain}$$

which is the desired answer since, by Newton's third law, the chain exerts a force of equal magnitude on the support.

(b)

$$T_0 = \frac{W}{2}\cot\theta \text{ Ans.}$$

14-6

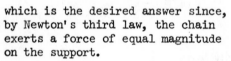

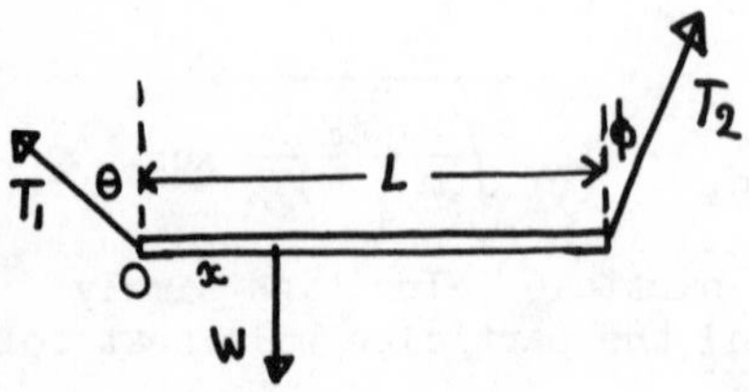

For translational equilibrium,

$$T_1\cos\theta + T_2\cos\phi = W,$$
$$T_1\sin\theta = T_2\sin\phi.$$

Taking moments about O,

$$Wx = (T_2\cos\phi)(L).$$

Noting that $\theta + \phi = 90°$ and solving gives

$$x = \frac{L}{1 + \tan\phi\cot\theta} = \frac{20\text{ ft}}{1 + \cot^2(36°54')} = 7.2\text{ ft Ans.}$$

14-11

The normal force $\vec{N}$ vanishes as the wheel lifts. Taking moments about O as this happens,

$$Wx = F(r - h).$$

But

$$x = \sqrt{r^2 - (r - h)^2} = \sqrt{h(2r - h)}$$

so that

$$F = W \frac{\sqrt{h(2r - h)}}{r - h} \quad \underline{\text{Ans.}}$$

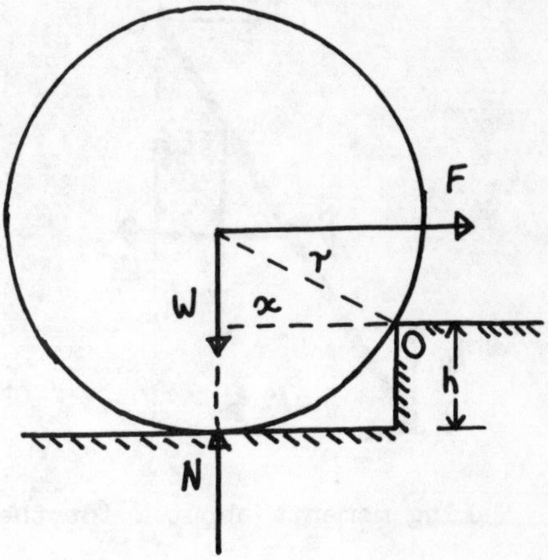

14-17

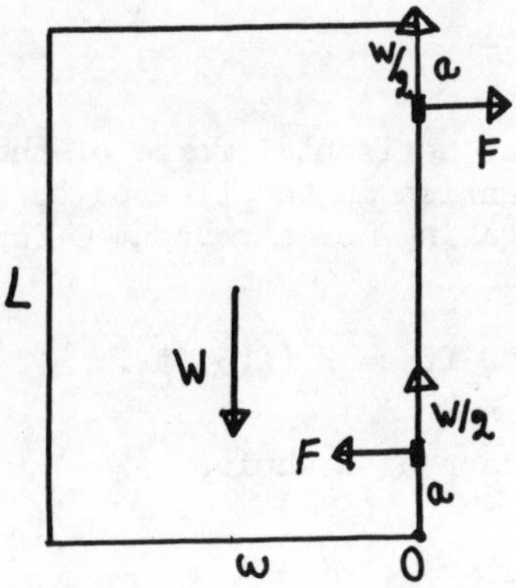

Since each hinge supports half the weight of the door, each upward force = $\frac{W}{2}$ = 30 lb Ans. The horizontal forces exerted by the hinges on the door are shown. Taking moments about O,

$$F(L - a) = F\,a + W\,\frac{w}{2},$$

$$F = \frac{(60 \text{ lb})(3 \text{ ft})}{2(7 - 2) \text{ ft}} = 18 \text{ lb} \quad \underline{\text{Ans.}}$$

14-23

On the following page we isolate the two legs of the ladder. Note that

$$d = \sqrt{4^2 - (5/4)^2} = 3.80 \text{ ft.}$$

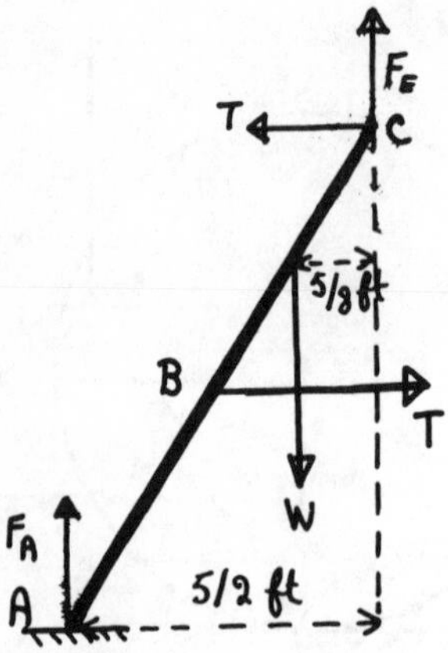

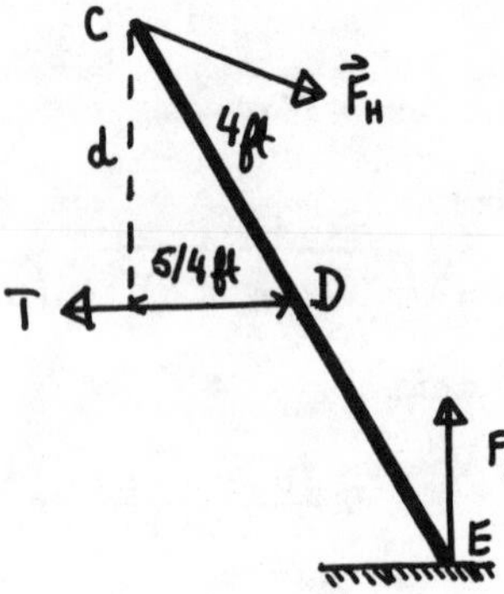

Taking moments about C for the right leg,

$$F_E(2.5\ \text{ft}) = T(3.80\ \text{ft}). \quad (*)$$

Also

$$\vec{F}_H = -\vec{F}_E - \vec{T}$$

so that the hinge is in equilibrium. The horizontal force of the hinge on the left leg must equal the tension in the tie rod to keep the leg in translational equilibrium. Taking moments about C for the left leg,

$$W\left(\frac{5}{8}\ \text{ft}\right) + T(3.80\ \text{ft}) = F_A(2.5\ \text{ft}). \quad (*)$$

For translational equilibium of the ladder as a whole,

$$W = F_A + F_E. \quad (*)$$

Putting W = 192 lb and solving the three indicated equations gives

(a) $T = 47$ lb Ans,

(b) $F_A = 120$ lb, $F_B = 72$ lb Ans.

14-24

The normal force $\vec{N}$ vanishes as the box begins to roll.

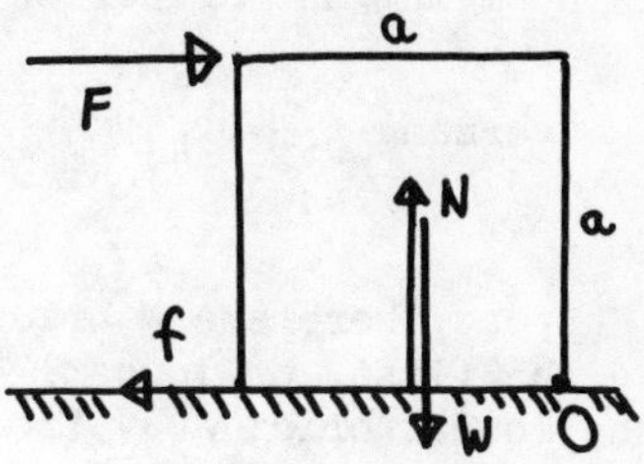

(a) For the minimum force choose the longest possible moment arm: i.e. push at the top. Taking moments about O,

$$W \frac{a}{2} = Fa \rightarrow F = \frac{W}{2} = 100 \text{ lb } \underline{\text{Ans.}}$$

(b) If the box was on the verge of slipping,

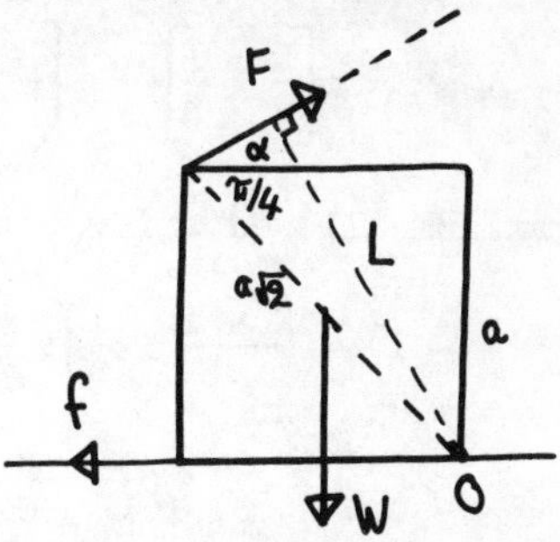

$$F = \mu_s N = \mu_s W \rightarrow \mu_s = \frac{F}{W},$$

$$\mu_s = 0.50 \ \underline{\text{Ans.}}$$

(c) If $\vec{F}$ is applied at an angle α above the horizontal at the top of the box then, again taking moments about O,

$$F\,L = W\frac{a}{2} \rightarrow F(a\sqrt{2})\sin(\alpha + \pi/4) = (200 \text{ lb})\,\frac{a}{2},$$

$$F \sin(\alpha + \pi/4) = 50\sqrt{2} \text{ lb}.$$

For F to be a minimum set $\sin(\alpha + \pi/4) = 1$, its maximum value. Thus $\alpha = \pi/4$ and

$$F = 50\sqrt{2} = 71 \text{ lb } \underline{\text{Ans.}}$$

14-26

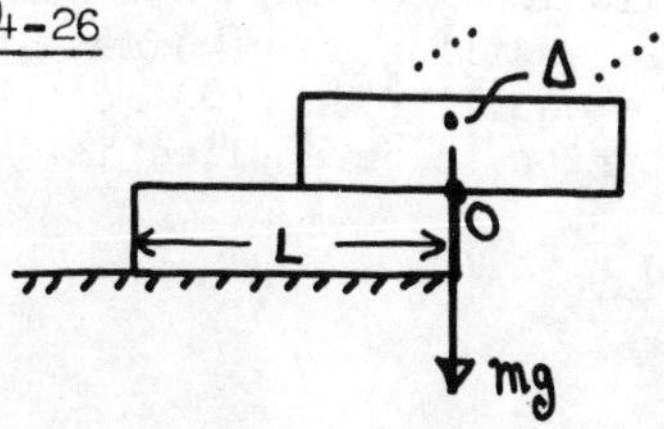

(a) Let Δ be the location of the center of mass of all the bricks above the bottom one. The moment of mg, though Δ, about O, the 'tipping' point is zero. If mg lies to the left of O the pile of bricks is stable, but if it lies to the right they will topple.

(b) By applying the criterion of (a),

$$\text{overhang} = \frac{L}{2} + \frac{L}{4} + \frac{L}{6} + \ldots = \frac{L}{2}\sum_{n=1}^{\infty}\frac{1}{n} \to \infty \quad \underline{\text{Ans.}}$$

(c) Suppose there are N bricks. The center of gravity of those above the first, or lowest, brick is at a distance x from that end of the lowest brick away from the overhang, where x satisfies the relation

$$(N - 1)mx = m\left[\frac{L}{2} + \frac{L}{n}\right] + m\left[\frac{L}{2} + \frac{2L}{n}\right] + \ldots + m\left[\frac{L}{2} + \frac{(N-1)L}{n}\right].$$

The maximum allowed x is just L; this leads to,

$$(N - 1) = \frac{N - 1}{2} + \frac{1}{n}\left[1 + 2 + 3 + \ldots + (N - 1)\right],$$

$$N - 1 = \frac{N - 1}{2} + \frac{1}{n}\frac{(N - 1)N}{2},$$

$$n = N \quad \underline{\text{Ans.}}$$

<u>14-28</u>

From the discussion in the text, the position of the cube shown in the figure will be stable if a small displacement causes the center of mass of the cube to rise, unstable if a small displacement causes it to fall. Since the cylindrical surface does not move, we can refer the vertical position of the cube's center of mass to O, the axis of the cylinder. As the cube is assumed to roll we can measure displacement by β, the angular displacement of the contact point with respect to O. Then, for stable equilibrium $h(\beta)$ must have a relative minimum at $\beta = 0$, for unstable equilibrium $h(\beta)$ must have a relative maximum there. Hence the criterion to be applied is:

$$\frac{d^2h}{d\beta^2} > 0 \text{ at } \beta = 0, \qquad \frac{d^2h}{d\beta^2} < 0 \text{ at } \beta = 0$$

for stable or unstable equilibrium respectively.
In the figure shown we let the **edges** of the cube be of length 2b: i.e. a = 2b. For no sliding we must have

$$\overline{QC'} = \widehat{CC'} \to b\tan\alpha = r\beta \to b\alpha = r\beta, \qquad (*)$$

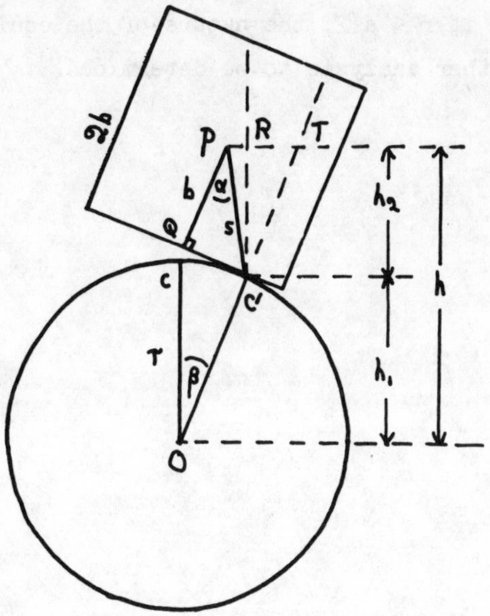

the last step since α is presumed to be small. Now $h = h_1 + h_2$ where $h_1 = r \cos\beta$. Note that OC'T is a straight line and C'R is a vertical line. Thus $\measuredangle PRC' = \pi/2$, $\measuredangle PC'T = \alpha$, $\measuredangle RC'T = \beta$ so that $\measuredangle PC'R = \alpha - \beta$. If we let $PC' = s$ then

$$C'R = h_2 = s \cos(\alpha - \beta).$$

But

$$s^2 = \overline{QP}^2 + \overline{QC'}^2 = b^2 + b^2\alpha^2 = b^2 + r^2\beta^2,$$

by (*). Thus, using (*) to eliminate α from h_2 we get

$$h = h_1 + h_2 = r \cos\beta + \sqrt{b^2 + r^2\beta^2}\, \cos(\frac{r}{b} - 1)\beta.$$

Now differentiate twice and then set $\beta = 0$ to obtain

$$\frac{d^2h}{d\beta^2} = r - b = r - \frac{a}{2}$$

at $\beta = 0$. Therefore we have stable equilibrium if $r > a/2$, unstable equilibrium if $r < a/2$; the nature of the equilibrium if $r = a/2$ requires further analysis to be determined.

15-11

If the block does not slip it too executes simple harmonic motion. We know then that the maximum force acting on it in the horizontal direction is

$$F_{max} = m\omega^2 A = 4\pi^2 m\nu^2 A.$$

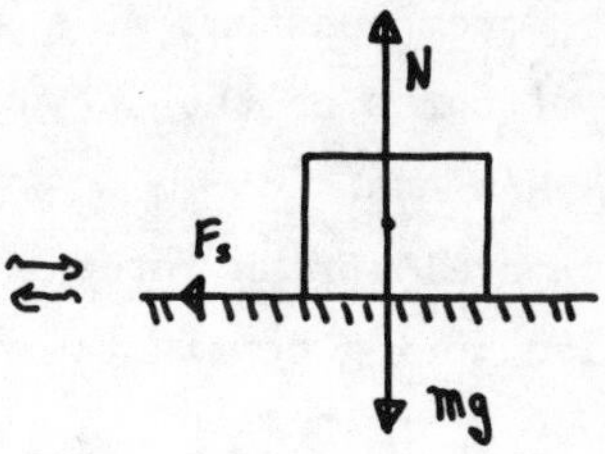

This force can be supplied only by static friction. If the amplitude A increases F_{max} increases also. But the force of friction F_s cannot increase without bound, for $F_s \leqslant \mu_s N$ where here N = mg. Hence the maximum amplitude A_{max} is given by

$$\mu_s mg = 4\pi^2 m\nu^2 A_{max} \rightarrow A_{max} = \mu_s g/4\pi^2\nu^2 = (0.5)(9.8\ \mathrm{m/s^2})/16\pi^2\ \mathrm{s^{-2}},$$

$$A_{max} = 0.031\ \mathrm{m} = 3.1\ \mathrm{cm}\ \underline{\mathrm{Ans.}}$$

15-15

Let the displacements of the particles be

$$x_1 = A\sin(\omega t + \delta_1), \qquad x_2 = A\sin(\omega t + \delta_2).$$

If the particles pass each other at t = 0, $x_1(0) = x_2(0) = A/2$ since they pass when their displacements are each half the amplitude. Thus,

$$\sin\delta_1 = \sin\delta_2 = 1/2 \rightarrow \delta_1 = 30°, 150°; \delta_2 = 30°, 150°.$$

But at t = 0, $v_1 = -v_2$ (opposite directions). This gives $\cos\delta_1 = -\cos\delta_2$. Hence we have either $\delta_1 = 30°$, $\delta_2 = 150°$ or $\delta_1 = 150°$, $\delta_2 = 30°$.

In any event, $|\delta_1 - \delta_2| = 120°$ Ans.

15-17

(a) The force constant of a spring is inversely proportional to the number of turns of the spring. Hence each piece has a force constant $k' = 14$ N/m Ans.

(b) The total spring force on the block is $2k'x = 4kx$. Thus the effective spring constant $K = 4k$. Therefore,

$$2\pi\nu = \sqrt{K/M} \rightarrow M = 4k/4\pi^2\nu^2 = (7\ \text{N/m})/\pi^2(3\ \text{s}^{-1}) = 0.079\ \text{kg Ans.}$$

15-21

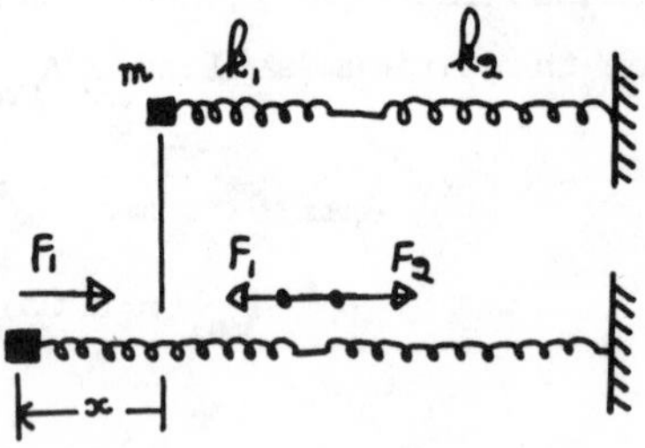

Spring 1 is stretched a distance x_1 and spring 2 a distance x_2; the mass m is displaced a distance x. We have then,

$$F_1 = k_1x_1,\ F_2 = k_2x_2,\ x = x_1 + x_2.$$

But, from Newton's third law

$$F_1 = F_2 \rightarrow k_1x_1 = k_2x_2$$

since each spring exerts a force on the other. Combining the equations above yields

$$x_1 = \frac{k_2}{k_1 + k_2}x.$$

The force on the mass m is $F_1 = k_1x_1$. Using the expression above we get the force of m in terms of the displacement of m. Then

$$\nu = \frac{1}{2\pi}\sqrt{\frac{k_1k_2}{(k_1 + k_2)m}}\ \text{Ans.}$$

15-22

(a) The separation at equilibrium is $r = b/a$ since $F(b/a) = 0$, meaning that the force is zero at this location.

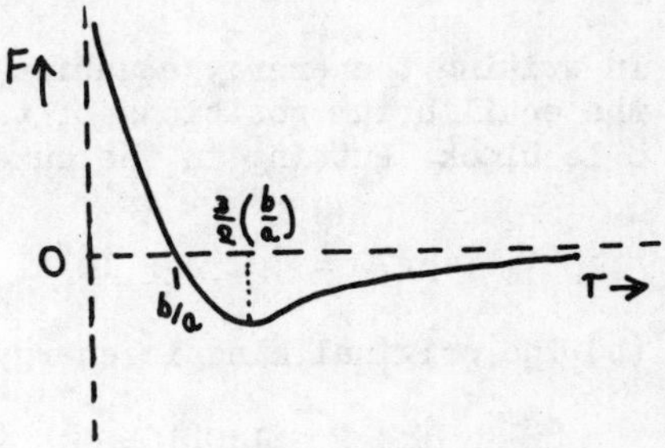

(b) Consider points only a small distance $x = r - b/a$ from the equilibrium point. The force at these points is

$$F(r) = -\frac{a}{(x + b/a)^2} + \frac{b}{(x + b/a)^3} = -\frac{a^3/b^2}{(1 + ax/b)^2} + \frac{a^3/b^2}{(1 + ax/b)^3}.$$

By assumption, $x/(b/a) = ax/b \ll 1$. Expanding in powers of ax/b and retaining only linear terms gives

$$F(r) \cong -(a^3/b^2)(1 - 2\frac{ax}{b}) + (a^3/b^2)(1 - 3\frac{ax}{b}) = -\frac{a^4}{b^3}x.$$

If we write this as $F = -kx$, the force constant $k = a^4/b^3$ Ans.

(c) The period T of simple harmonic motion is

$$T = 2\pi\sqrt{m/k} = 2\pi\sqrt{(mb^3)/(a^4)} \quad \text{Ans.}$$

15-28

Let m, w be the mass and weight of the bullet and M, W the same quantities for the block. By conservation of momentum,

$$wv = (w + W)V \rightarrow V = \frac{w}{w + W}v = \frac{0.1\text{ lb}}{8.1\text{ lb}}(500\text{ ft/s}) = 6.17\text{ ft/s}.$$

(a) Conservation of energy gives

$$\frac{1}{2}(m + M)V^2 + \frac{1}{2}kx_i^{\,2} = (m + M)gA + \frac{1}{2}kA^2,$$

where x_i is the initial extension of the spring: this is

$$x_i = Mg/k = (8\ \text{lb})/(36\ \text{lb/ft}) = 0.222\ \text{ft}.$$

In writing the energy equation we neglected the difference between the equilibrium positions of the 8.1 lb block (+ bullet) and the 8 lb block. Putting in the numerical values yields

$$5.70 = 8.1\ A + 18\ A^2 \quad \rightarrow \quad A = 0.38\ \text{ft} = 4.6\ \text{in}\ \underline{\text{Ans.}}$$

(b) The original kinetic energy of the bullet is

$$K_i = \frac{1}{2}mv^2 = \frac{1}{2}(\frac{0.10}{32}\ \text{slug})(500\ \text{ft/s})^2 = 390.6\ \text{ft}\cdot\text{lb},$$

and the total energy of the oscillator is

$$\frac{1}{2}kA^2 = \frac{1}{2}(36\ \text{lb/ft})(0.38\ \text{ft})^2 = 2.60\ \text{ft}\cdot\text{lb}.$$

Hence the desired fraction is simply

$$2.60/390.6 = 0.67\%\ \underline{\text{Ans.}}$$

<u>15-30</u>

The translational kinetic energy is just

$$K_t = \frac{1}{2}Mv^2;$$

the rotational kinetic energy is

$$K_r = \frac{1}{2}I\omega^2 = \frac{1}{2}(\frac{1}{2}MR^2)(v/R)^2 = \frac{1}{4}Mv^2;$$

the potential energy is, of course,

$$U = \frac{1}{2}kx^2.$$

Hence the total energy becomes

$$E = \frac{3}{4}Mv^2 + \frac{1}{2}kx^2.$$

The system was released from rest so that $v_i = 0$. Hence

$$E = \frac{1}{2}(3\ \text{N/m})(0.25\ \text{m})^2 = \frac{3}{32}\ \text{J}.$$

At equilibrium x = 0, and therefore by energy conservation,

$$E = \frac{3}{4} Mv_e^{\ 2} = \frac{3}{32}\ \text{J} \rightarrow Mv_e^{\ 2} = \frac{1}{8}\ \text{J}.$$

Therefore (a) K_t = (1/16) J = 0.063 J Ans, and (b) K_r = (1/32) J = 0.031 J Ans.

(b) As before we have

$$E = \frac{3}{4} Mv^2 + \frac{1}{2} kx^2.$$

Differentiate with respect to time and factor out $\dot{x} = v$ to get,

$$\frac{3}{4} M\ddot{x} + \frac{1}{2} kx = 0 \rightarrow \ddot{x} + \frac{2k}{3M} x = 0.$$

This is of the form $\ddot{x} + \omega^2 x = 0$ so that the period must be

$$T = 2\pi/\omega = 2\pi \sqrt{\frac{3M}{2k}} \quad \text{Ans.}$$

15-31

We use the following notation:

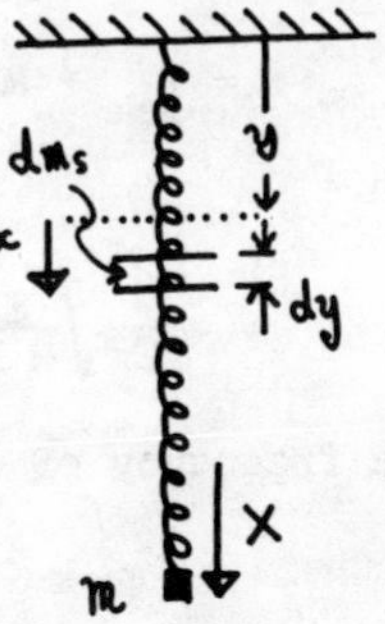

x = extension of an element of the spring located a distance y from the fixed end, if unstretched;

X = extension of the spring at the moving end;

L = unstretched length of spring.

The potential energy of the system is

$$V = \frac{1}{2} kX^2,$$

whilst the kinetic energy can be written

$$T = \frac{1}{2} m\dot{X}^2 + \frac{1}{2}\int \dot{x}^2 \, dm_s = \frac{1}{2} m\dot{X}^2 + \frac{1}{2}\int \dot{x}^2 (m_s/L) dy.$$

By assumption,

$$\frac{x}{X} = \frac{y}{L} \rightarrow \dot{x} = \frac{y}{L}\dot{X} \rightarrow T = \frac{1}{2} m\dot{X}^2 + \frac{1}{2}\frac{m_s}{L}\frac{\dot{X}^2}{L^2}\int_0^L y^2 \, dy,$$

$$T = \frac{1}{2}(m + m_s/3)\dot{X}^2.$$

Now invoke conservation of energy and differentiate with respect to time:

$$\frac{1}{2} kX^2 + \frac{1}{2}(m + m_s/3)\dot{X}^2 = E \rightarrow kX\dot{X} + (m + m_s/3)\dot{X}\ddot{X} = 0,$$

$$\ddot{X} + \frac{k}{m + m_s/3} X = 0 \rightarrow T = 2\pi\sqrt{\frac{(m + m_s/3)}{k}} \quad \underline{\text{Ans.}}$$

15-35

For a physical pendulum,

$$\nu = \frac{1}{2\pi} \frac{MgR}{I} .$$

By the parallel-axis theorem the rotational inertia I about the point of support is

$$I = I_{cm} + Mh^2 = MR^2 + MR^2 = 2\,MR^2.$$

Therefore

(a) $$\nu = \frac{1}{2\pi}\sqrt{\frac{g}{2\,R}} = \frac{1}{2\pi}\sqrt{\frac{(32\text{ ft/s}^2)}{4\text{ ft}}} = 0.45\text{ Hz} \quad \underline{\text{Ans.}}$$

(b) The frequency of a simple pendulum is

$$\nu_s = \frac{1}{2\pi}\sqrt{\frac{g}{L}} .$$

For $\nu = \nu_s$ we need $L = 2\,R = 4$ ft Ans.

15-37

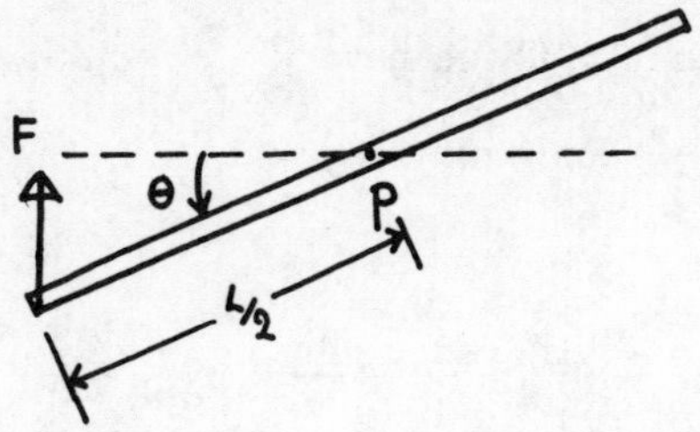

The torque exerted by the spring about the pivot P is

$$\tau = \frac{L}{2} F = - kx \frac{L}{2} = - k(\frac{L}{2} \theta) \frac{L}{2}$$

$$= - k \frac{L^2}{4} \theta = I\alpha = I\ddot{\theta}$$

if the angle θ is small. Since $I = \frac{1}{12} ML^2$ we get

$$- k \frac{L^2}{4} \theta = \frac{1}{12} ML^2 \ddot{\theta} \rightarrow \ddot{\theta} + \frac{3 k}{M} \theta = 0.$$

Identifying the coefficient of θ with ω^2 gives for the period T,

$$T = 2\pi\sqrt{\frac{M}{3 k}} \quad \underline{\text{Ans.}}$$

15-38

We represent the displacement of the wheel by $\theta = \theta_m \cos(\omega t + \delta)$. Here $\theta_m = \pi$ and $\nu = 1/T = 1/(0.5 \text{ s}) = 2$ Hz so that $\omega = 4\pi$ rad/s. Hence we have

$$\theta = \pi \cos(4\pi t + \delta).$$

Note that the ω here = 2π(number of oscillations per second) is not dθ/dt, the angular velocity. This difference in notation over previous chapters must be borne in mind. We do still use α for angular acceleration = $d^2\theta/dt^2$.

(a) Differentiating, $d\theta/dt = - (\pi)(4\pi)\sin(4\pi t + \delta)$. Hence $\left|\frac{d\theta}{dt}\right|_{max} = 4\pi^2$ rad/s Ans.

(b) When the displacement θ is π/2 we have (if this happens at t = t'),

$$\pi/2 = \pi \cos(4\pi t' + \delta) \rightarrow \cos(4\pi t' + \delta) = 1/2.$$

It follows that $\sin(4\pi t' + \delta) = \sqrt{3}/2$ so that

$$v(t') = -4\pi^2 \sin(4\pi t' + \delta) = -4\pi^2\sqrt{3}/2 = -2\pi^2\sqrt{3}\ \text{rad/s}\ \underline{\text{Ans.}}$$

(c) If the displacement $\theta = \pi/4$ when $t = t''$ we have

$$\pi/4 = \pi \cos(4\pi t'' + \delta) \rightarrow \cos(4\pi t'' + \delta) = 1/4.$$

Therefore

$$\alpha(t'') = -(4\pi)^2\pi \cos(4\pi t'' + \delta) = -4\pi^3\ \text{rad/s}^2\ \underline{\text{Ans.}}$$

15-42

(a) The equation of motion of the rod is

$$\tau = mgd \sin\theta \cong mgd\ \theta = -I\ddot{\theta} \rightarrow \ddot{\theta} + \frac{mgd}{I}\theta = 0,$$

so that

$$\omega^2 = mgd/I.$$

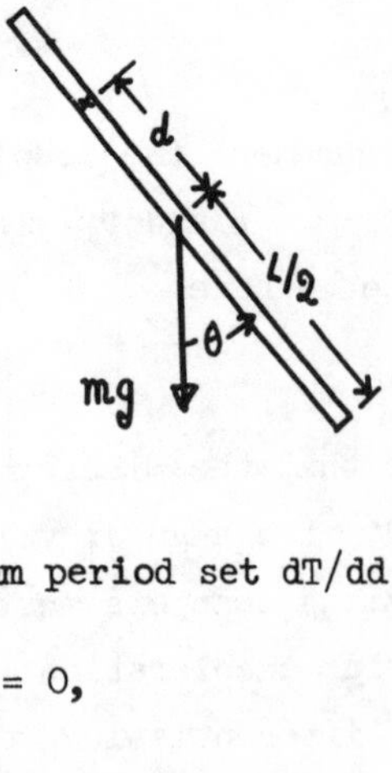

By the parallel-axis theorem,

$$I = I_{cm} + mh^2 = \frac{1}{12} mL^2 + md^2$$

and therefore the period T is

$$T = \frac{2\pi}{\omega} = 2\pi\sqrt{\frac{L^2 + 12\ d^2}{12\ gd}}\ \underline{\text{Ans.}}$$

(b) To find the value of d giving the minimum period set $dT/dd = 0$:

$$\frac{dT}{dd} = 4\pi^2 \frac{1}{2}\frac{1}{T}\frac{1}{12g}\left[\frac{24d}{d} - \frac{L^2 + 12\ d^2}{d^2}\right] = 0,$$

$$24\ d^2 - (L^2 + 12\ d^2) = 0 \rightarrow d = L/\sqrt{12}\ \underline{\text{Ans.}}$$

15-45

By the path of the electrons, it is meant that we want y vs x: i.e. eliminate t. This may easily be done for if $x = A\cos\omega t$, $y = A\cos(\omega t + \alpha)$ we have

$$y = A(\cos\omega t \cos\alpha - \sin\omega t \sin\alpha) = A\left[\frac{x}{A}\cos\alpha - \sqrt{1 - x^2/A^2}\right]\sin\alpha .$$

Rearrange and square:

$$y - x\cos\alpha = -A\sqrt{1 - x^2/A^2}\,\sin\alpha,$$

$$y^2 - 2xy\cos\alpha + x^2\cos^2\alpha = A^2(1 - x^2/A^2)\sin^2\alpha.$$

But $\sin^2\alpha + \cos^2\alpha = 1$ and therefore we have finally

$$y^2 - 2xy\cos\alpha + x^2 = A^2\sin^2\alpha.$$

This is the equation of an ellipse and, since it remains unchanged if x and y are interchanged, the axis of the ellipse must make angles of 45° with the x and y axes.

(a) $\alpha = 0$. The equation becomes $y = x$, the ellipse degenerating to a straight line.

(b) $\alpha = 30°$. We see the tilted ellipse.

(c) $\alpha = 90°$. Here we get $x^2 + y^2 = A^2$, a circle of radius A.

15-48

(a) The trajectory is shown in the sketch.

(b) Since $\vec{r} = A(\vec{i}\cos\omega t + \vec{j}\cos 3\omega t)$ we have

$$\vec{v} = \frac{d\vec{r}}{dt} = -\omega A(\vec{i}\sin\omega t + \vec{j}\,3\sin 3\omega t)$$

and therefore $\vec{L} = m\vec{r} \times \vec{v}$ is just

$$\vec{L} = -mA^2\omega(3\sin 3\omega t\cos\omega t - \sin\omega t\cos 3\omega t)$$ Ans.

(c) Since $\vec{F} = m\vec{a}$ we need only differentiate $\vec{v}$:

$$\vec{F} = -m\omega^2 A(\vec{i}\cos\omega t + \vec{j}\,9\cos 3\omega t)$$ Ans.

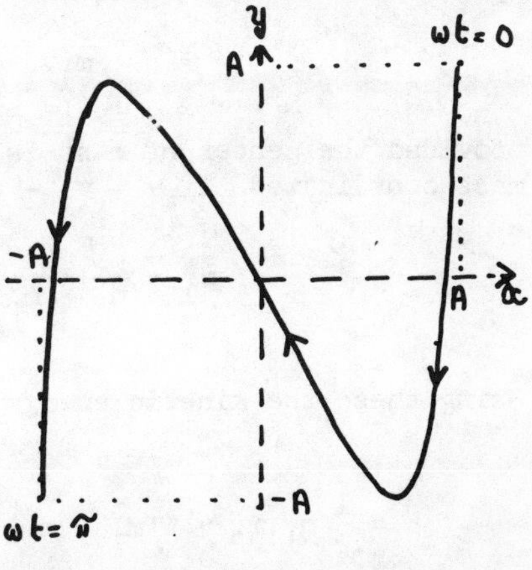

Particle returns over same path.

(d) For this particle $x = A\cos\omega t$ and $y = A\cos 3\omega t$. Hence, from (d),

$$F_x = -m\omega^2 x = -\frac{\partial U}{\partial x} \rightarrow U = \frac{1}{2} m\omega^2 x^2 + f(y),$$

$$F_y = -9m\omega^2 y = -\frac{\partial U}{\partial y} \rightarrow U = \frac{9}{2} m\omega^2 y^2 + g(x).$$

Comparing these two expressions for U we conclude that

$$U = \frac{1}{2} m\omega^2(x^2 + 9y^2) = \frac{1}{2} mA^2\omega^2(\cos^2\omega t + 9 \cos^2 3\omega t) \text{ \underline{Ans.}}$$

(e) The kinetic energy is simply

$$K = \frac{1}{2} mv^2 = \frac{1}{2} m\omega^2 A^2(\sin^2\omega t + 9 \sin^2 3\omega t).$$

Since the total energy $E = U + K$ and $\sin^2\theta + \cos^2\theta = 1$ we get

$$E = 5\, m\omega^2 A^2 \text{ \underline{Ans.}}$$

(f) The motion is periodic with period $T = 2\pi/\omega$ Ans.

15-53

By conservation of momentum

$$m_1 v_1 + m_2 v_2 = 0,$$

provided the center of mass is at rest; if it is not, use center of mass coordinates. If $v = v_1 - v_2$ is the relative velocity we obtain

$$v_1 = \frac{m_2 v}{m_1 + m_2}, \quad v_2 = \frac{m_1 v}{m_1 + m_2}.$$

Using these the kinetic energy $K = \frac{1}{2} m_1 v_1^2 + \frac{1}{2} m_2 v_2^2$ becomes

$$K = \frac{1}{2} m_1\, m_2^2 v^2/(m_1 + m_2)^2 + \frac{1}{2} m_2\, m_1^2 v^2/(m_1 + m_2)^2,$$

$$K = \frac{1}{2} \frac{m_1 m_2}{m_1 + m_2} v^2 = \frac{1}{2}\mu v^2 \text{ \underline{Ans.}}$$

15-54

The displacement of the block is given by

$$x = Ae^{-bt/2m}\cos(\omega' t + \delta).$$

If the amplitude falls to one-third of its initial value t' seconds after the motion begins, then

$$\frac{1}{3}A = Ae^{-bt'/2m} \rightarrow t' = \frac{2m}{b}\ln 3.$$

The number N of oscillations completed in this time is

$$N = \nu t' = \frac{\omega'}{2\pi}t' = \frac{\omega'}{2\pi}\frac{2m}{b}\ln 3 = \frac{\omega'}{\pi}\frac{m}{b}\ln 3.$$

Evaluating ω',

$$\omega' = \sqrt{k/m - (b/2m)^2} = \sqrt{(8/1.5) - (0.23/3)^2} = 2.31 \text{ rad/s},$$

and therefore

$$N = \frac{2.31}{\pi}\frac{1.5}{0.23}(1.099) = 5.3$$ Ans.

16-8

(a) If R is the radius of the earth the difference in weight is

$$W' - W = GMm/R^2 - GMm/(R + h)^2.$$

Clearly we have $h/R \ll 1$ and therefore can write this as

$$W' - W \cong \frac{GMm}{R^2} - \frac{GMm}{R^2}(1 - 2\frac{h}{R}) = 2GMm\, h/R^3 = \frac{8\pi}{3} G\rho mh \text{ Ans,}$$

since $M = \frac{4\pi}{3} R^3\rho$.

(b) Solving (a) for h,

$$h = (W' - W)/(8\pi G\rho m/3) = \frac{W' - W}{W}\frac{3g}{8\pi G\rho}.$$

Putting $(W' - W)/W = 10^{-6}$ and substituting the numerical values $g = 980\ \text{cm/s}^2$, $G = 6.67 \times 10^{-8}\ \text{dyne·cm}^2/\text{g}^2$ and $\rho = 5.5\ \text{g/cm}^3$ yields $h = 319\ \text{cm} = 3.2\ \text{m}$ Ans.

16-13

For a circular orbit and assuming that the stars of the galaxy are distributed in space in a spherically symmetric manner (which they are not) we will have

$$G M_{gal}M_s/R^2 = M_s\, v^2/R$$

where v is the speed of the sun in its orbit and R is the distance to the galactic center. The period T of revolution is

$$T = \frac{2\pi R}{v} = 2\pi(R^3/GM_{gal})^{1/2} \rightarrow M_{gal} = \frac{4\pi^2}{G}\frac{R^3}{T^2},$$

$$M_{gal} = \frac{4\pi^2}{6.67 \times 10^{-11}\ \text{N·m}^2/\text{kg}^2}\frac{(2.4 \times 10^{20}\ \text{m})^3}{(7.9 \times 10^{15}\ \text{s})^2} = 1.3 \times 10^{41}\ \text{kg}.$$

The mass M_s of the sun is 2×10^{30} kg and if this is typical of the stars in the galaxy their number N will be approximately

$$N = (1.3 \times 10^{41})/(2 \times 10^{30}) = 6.5 \times 10^{10} \text{ \underline{Ans.}}$$

Strictly speaking, this gives an estimate only of the number of stars in the galaxy lying interior to the orbit of the sun.

16-14

Let m, M refer to the falling object and the earth, respectively. Then, in a fixed inertial frame centered at the center of mass of earth + object, we have

$$G \frac{m\,M}{(r_m + r_M)^2} = m\,a_m, \qquad G \frac{m\,M}{(r_m + r_M)^2} = M\,a_M.$$

These expressions indicate that a_m is independent of m but not of M and that a_M is independent of M but not of m. But

$$a_m + a_M = GM/(r_m + r_M)^2 + Gm/(r_m + r_M)^2$$

$$a_m + a_M = G(m + M)/(r_m + r_M)^2$$

so that $a_m + a_M$, the relative acceleration, depends on m + M. Therefore, the statement that g is the same regardless of the mass of the falling body means g relative to the center of mass, the scource mass (M) being kept constant. The earth is not a fixed, inertial reference frame. However, the Galilean conclusion that all bodies fall at the same rate is almost exactly right for $m \ll M$ but is fundamentally right vis-a-vis Aristotle; this would clearly be shown by dropping equal masses m (successively increasing m in successive trials) toward the earth from opposite sides of the earth (the earth is then at the center of mass and still $m \ll M$).

16-17

(a) The component of the gravitational force $\vec{F}$ on the object directed along the chord is $F\cos\beta = F(x/r)$ towards x = 0. But if M_r is the mass of the earth interior to r and Δ is the density of

the earth (assumed uniform), we have

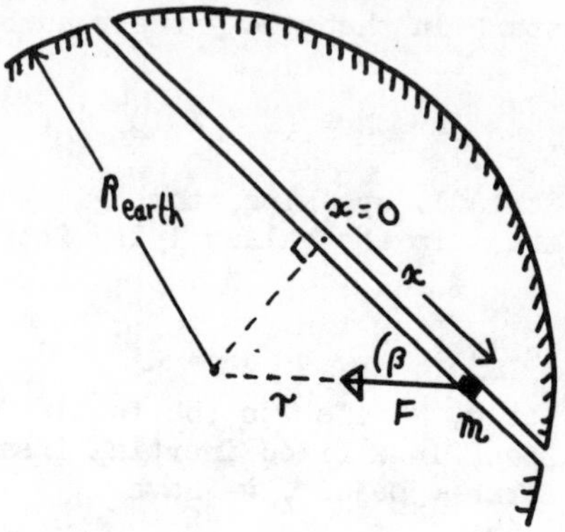

$$F = GM_r m/r^2 = G(\tfrac{4}{3}\pi r^3 \Delta)m/r^2,$$

$$F = \frac{4}{3}\pi G\Delta m r.$$

Therefore

$$F\cos\beta = (\tfrac{4}{3}\pi G\Delta m)x = -m\frac{d^2x}{dt^2},$$

the minus sign since the force is always directed toward $x = 0$.
This is an equation describing simple harmonic motion with a frequency ν given by

$$\nu^2 = \frac{G\Delta}{3\pi}.$$

(b) By comparison with the case of a chute dug along a diameter we find the two frequencies to be equal. Hence the periods $T = 1/\nu = 84.2$ min are the same also Ans.

(c) In simple harmonic motion $v_{max} = 2\pi A/T$. In this case the amplitude $A = \frac{1}{2}$(chord length) $< R_{earth}$ which is the amplitude for a chute along a diameter. Since the periods are the same for motion along chord and diameter v_{max} will be less for the former case Ans.

16-18

(a) Let the mass of the particle at P be m, and $d\gamma$ the solid angle of the narrow double cone constructed with apex at P. The cone intercepts areas dA_1 and dA_2 on the surface of the shell (of density Δ). Note that these areas are not perpendicular to the generators of the cone: thus we construct areas dA_1' and dA_2' which are perpendicular. The areas dA_1 and dA_2 are so small that Newton's law of universal gravitation can be applied to them. The force on m due to dA_1 is

$dF_1 = Gm\Delta(dA_1)/(QP)^2$, along $\overrightarrow{PQ}$.

The force on m due to dA_2 is

$dF_2 = Gm\Delta(dA_2)/(RP)^2$, along $\overrightarrow{PR}$.

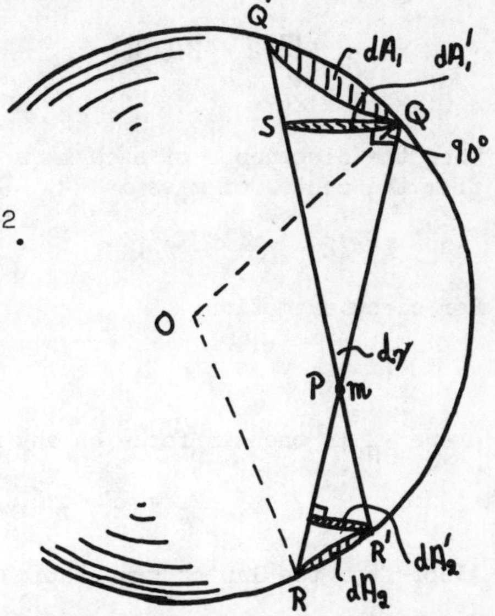

But

$d\gamma = dA_1'/(QP)^2 = dA_1 \cos\sphericalangle Q'QS/(QP)^2$.

Since $\sphericalangle OQQ' = \sphericalangle SQP = \pi/2$ we have $\sphericalangle Q'QS = \sphericalangle OQP$ and therefore

$$d\gamma = dA_1 \cos\sphericalangle OQP/(QP)^2,$$
$$dA_1 = (QP)^2 \sec\sphericalangle OQP \, d\gamma.$$

Similarly $dA_2 = (RP)^2 \sec\sphericalangle ORP \, d\gamma$.
Thus we have

$$dF_1 = Gm\Delta(QP)^2 \sec\sphericalangle OQP \, d\gamma/(QP)^2 = Gm\Delta \sec\sphericalangle OQP \, d\gamma,$$
$$dF_2 = Gm\Delta(RP)^2 \sec\sphericalangle ORP \, d\gamma/(RP)^2 = Gm\Delta \sec< ORP \, d\gamma.$$

But $\overline{OR} = \overline{OQ}$ and thus $\sphericalangle OQP = \sphericalangle ORP$ and $dF_1 = dF_2$, or $d\vec{F}_1 + d\vec{F}_2 = 0$.
(b) The entire shell may be divided into similar pairs of areas by taking cones in all directions around P. Thus the net force on m is zero.

16-25

From the second law,

$$F = m\frac{v^2}{r} = \frac{m}{r}\left(\frac{2\pi r}{T}\right)^2 = 4\pi^2 m\, r/T^2 = k\, r/r^3 = k/r^2,$$

since, from Kepler's third law, T^2 is proportional to r^3. Here k is a constant.

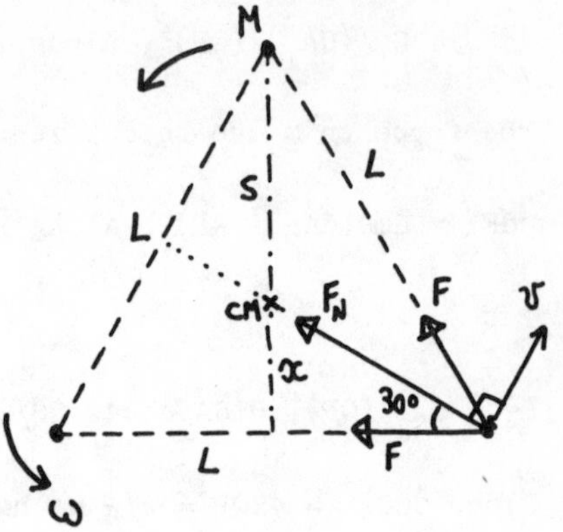

16-27

First locate the center of mass of the system:

$$3M\,x = M\,L\sqrt{3}/2 + 2M(0),$$

$$x = L\sqrt{3}/6.$$

Then the distance s of each mass from the center of mass is

$$s = L\sqrt{3}/2 - x = L\sqrt{3}/3.$$

For circular motion

$$F_N = M\,v^2/s$$

where F_N is the net force on any mass. But

$$F_N = 2F\cos 30° = 2F\sqrt{3}/2 = F\sqrt{3}.$$

Also, from the law of gravitation,

$$F = GM^2/L^2\ .$$

Therefore:

$$\frac{GM^2}{L^2}\sqrt{3} = M\,v^2/s = M\,v^2/(L\sqrt{3}/3) = \sqrt{3}\,M\,v^2/L,$$

Solving for v gives

$$v = \sqrt{GM/L}\ \underline{\text{Ans.}}$$

16-34

(a) The escape velocity at the earth's surface is $v_e = \sqrt{2GM_e/R_e}$. Since $g = GM_e/R_e^2$ we have $v_e = \sqrt{2gR_e}$. Since the speed of the rocket was $v = 2\sqrt{gR_e} > v_e$ the rocket escapes.

(b) By conservation of energy

$$\frac{1}{2}\,mv^2 - GM_e m/R_e = \frac{1}{2}\,mV^2 - 0,$$

the potential energy being nearly zero when the rocket is very far from the earth. Solving for V gives us,

$$V^2 = v^2 - 2GM_e/R_e = 4gR_e - 2gR_e = 2gR_e,$$

$$V = \sqrt{2gR_e} \text{ \underline{Ans.}}$$

16-37

Let i, f refer to the initial configuration and to the configuration when the separation of the particles is d. Then,

$$\Delta U = U_f - U_i = -\frac{GMm}{d} - 0, \quad \Delta K = \frac{1}{2} mv^2 + \frac{1}{2} MV^2 - 0,$$

where v, V are the speeds relative to some fixed coordinate system. By conservation of energy $\Delta U + \Delta K = 0$ sc that

$$\frac{GMm}{d} = \frac{1}{2} mv^2 + \frac{1}{2} MV^2.$$

Now the initial momentum was zero; thus to conserve momentum we must have

$$mv = MV.$$

Then the energy equation becomes,

$$\frac{GMm}{d} = \frac{1}{2} mv(v + V).$$

Let the relative speed be u; it can be expressed in terms of v:

$$u = v + V = v + \frac{m}{M} v = \frac{m + M}{M} v.$$

Therefore,

$$\frac{GMm}{d} = \frac{1}{2} m \left(\frac{Mu}{m + M}\right)u = \frac{1}{2} \frac{Mm}{m + M} u^2,$$

$$u = \sqrt{2G(m + M)/d} \text{ \underline{Ans.}}$$

16-38

The distance a, the radius of the earth's orbit, is 1 AU (astronomical unit). Let t be the time for the comet to move from D to B. If dA/dt = the rate at which a line from sun to comet sweeps out area and $\mathcal{Q}$ = the area of sector BCD of the parabola, then

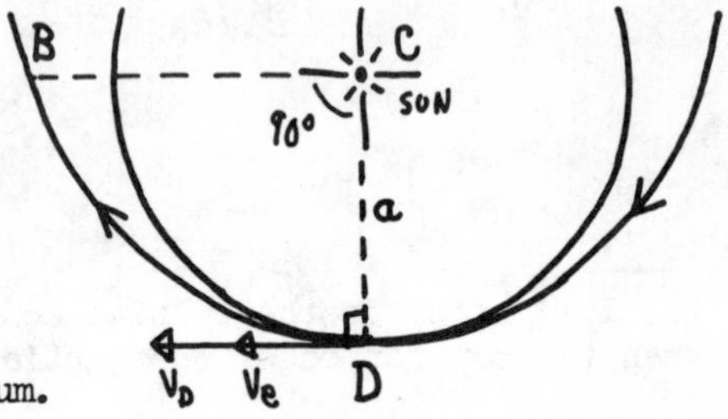

$$\mathcal{Q} = \frac{dA}{dt}\, t,$$

by conservation of angular momentum. Since dA/dt is a constant we can evaluate it at D.

$$\frac{dA}{dt} = \frac{1}{2}\omega r^2 = \frac{1}{2}(v_D/r_D)r_D{}^2 = \frac{1}{2}\, r_D v_D = \frac{1}{2}\, a\, v_D.$$

Now let v_e be the speed of the earth in its orbit and dA_e/dt the rate at which the earth sweeps out area. By problem 16 - 31,

$$dA/dt = \frac{1}{2}\, av_D = \frac{1}{2}\, a(\sqrt{2}v_e) = \sqrt{2}(\frac{1}{2}\, av_e).$$

But the factor in parenthesis is just dA_e/dt:

$$dA/dt = \sqrt{2}\, dA_e/dt = \sqrt{2}\,\pi\, (1\text{ AU})^2/\text{yr} = \pi\sqrt{2}\text{ AU}^2/\text{yr}.$$

The area $\mathcal{Q}$ of the sector BCD of a parabola is $\frac{4}{3}\, a^2$. Since a = 1 AU we have

$$\frac{4}{3}\text{ AU}^2 = \pi\sqrt{2}\, t\text{ AU}^2 \rightarrow t = 4/3\pi\sqrt{2}\text{ yrs } \underline{\text{Ans.}}$$

16-43

We let R_e, R_m be the radii of the earth and moon and d the distance between their centers.

(a) The potential energies add as scalars:

$$U = -\, GM_e m/R - GM_m m/r\ \underline{\text{Ans.}}$$

(b) The field will be zero for a point between earth and moon located by

$$GM_e m/R^2 = GM_m m/r^2 = GM_m m/(d - R)^2.$$

Since $M_e = 81\ M_m$ this gives $R = (9/10)d$ Ans.

In the following we assume that the point considered lies on the line joining the centers of the earth and moon. At either of the locations of interest the forces due to the earth and moon are in opposite directions.

(c) On the earth's surface $R = R_e$, $r = d - R_e$ and so we have

$$U = -GM_e m/R_e - GM_m m/(d - R_e),$$
$$g = GM_e/R_e^{\ 2} - GM_m/(d - R_e)^2, \text{ toward earth's center} \qquad \text{Ans.}$$

(d) At the moon's surface $r = R_m$, $R = d - R_m$ giving

$$U = -GM_e m/(d - R_m) - GM_m m/R_m,$$
$$g = GM_m/R_m^{\ 2} - GM_e/(d - R_m)^2, \text{ toward moon's center} \qquad \text{Ans.}$$

16-47

Let r_m, r_M be the distances of m and M from their center of mass. Then, since $d = r_m + r_M$,

(a)

$$GmM/d^2 = Mv_M^{\ 2}/r_M = Mr_M\omega^2, \quad GmM/d^2 = mr_m\omega^2.$$

Adding these,

$$G(m + M)/d^2 = (r_m + r_M)\omega^2 = (2\pi/T)^2 d \rightarrow T^2 = \frac{4\pi^2}{G}\frac{d^3}{m + M}.$$

With $M = 2m$ this becomes

$$T = 2\pi d^{3/2}/\sqrt{3Gm} \text{ Ans.}$$

(b) Since the orbits are circular $L = mvr$ so that

$$\frac{L_m}{L_M} = \frac{mv_m r_m}{Mv_M r_M} = \frac{1}{2}(v_m/v_M)\frac{2}{1} = \sqrt{\frac{GMr_m/d^2}{Gmr_M/d^2}} = \sqrt{Mr_m/mr_M} = \sqrt{\frac{2}{1}\,\frac{2}{1}} = 2 \text{ Ans.}$$

(c) By straightforward calculation,

$$K_m/K_M = \frac{1}{2} mv_m^2/\frac{1}{2} Mv_M^2 = \frac{m}{M}(v_m/v_M)^2 = \frac{1}{2}(2)^2 = 2 \text{ } \underline{\text{Ans}}.$$

16-49

At the extreme positions, denoted 1 and 2, the velocity is perpendicular to the radius vector.

(a) By conservation of angular momentum,

$$mr_1v_1 = mr_2v_2 \rightarrow r_1v_1 = a\sqrt{k/2ma}.$$

Conservation of energy gives,

$$\frac{1}{2} mv_1^2 - \frac{k}{r_1} = \frac{1}{2} mv_2^2 - \frac{k}{r_2} = \frac{1}{2} m(\frac{k}{2ma}) - \frac{k}{a} = - \frac{3}{4}\frac{k}{a},$$

$$\frac{1}{2} mv_1^2 = \frac{k}{r_1} - \frac{3}{4}\frac{k}{a}.$$

But $r_1^2v_1^2 = ka/2m$. Thus

$$r_1^2 = \frac{ka/2m}{\frac{2}{m}(\frac{k}{r_1} - \frac{3}{4}\frac{k}{a})} \rightarrow r_1^2 - \frac{4a}{3} r_1 + \frac{a^2}{3} = 0.$$

Factoring this yields

$$(r_1 - a)(r_1 - \frac{a}{3}) = 0 \rightarrow r_1 = \frac{a}{3} \text{ } \underline{\text{Ans}}.$$

(b) From the momentum equation,

$$v_1 = a\sqrt{k/2ma} \,/\frac{a}{3} = 3\sqrt{k/2ma} \text{ } \underline{\text{Ans}}.$$

16-50

(a) The northern edge of the floor of a room in the northern hemisphere is nearer the axis of rotation of the earth than is the southern edge, and therefore its linear velocity due to the earth's rotation is less than for the southern edge since the circumference of its path is smaller. Thus the floor twists around continually, everywhere except at the earth's equator. The pendulum is constrained to follow the changes in the direction of $\vec{g}$, i.e. the vertical, but is otherwise free. Its plane of oscillation, therefore, will appear to rotate in the opposite direction to the twisting of the ground and at the same rate.

(b) The vertical component of $\vec{\omega}$ at latitude θ is $\omega \sin\theta$. Thus the earth appears to rotate beneath the pendulum with a period

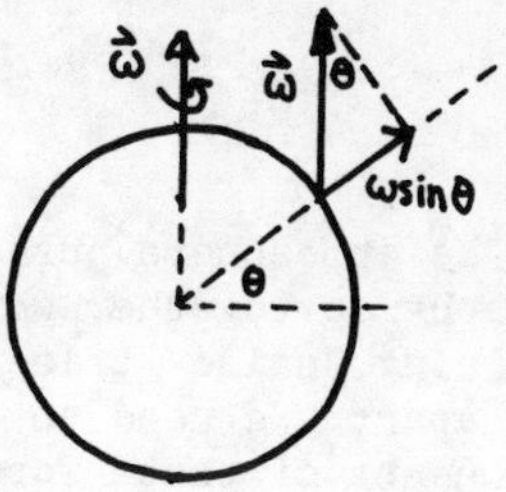

$$T = \frac{2\pi}{\omega \sin\theta} = \frac{24\ \text{h}}{\sin\theta} \quad \underline{\text{Ans}},$$

or, as seen from the earth, the pendulum appears to rotate in that time.

(c)

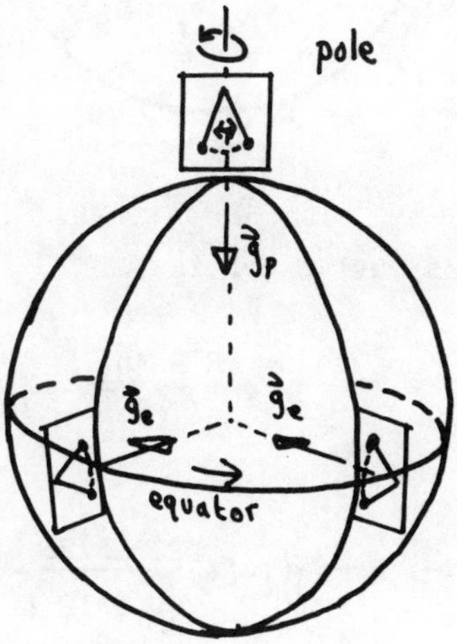

At the poles the plane of oscillation is fixed and the earth rotates beneath it: thus T = 24 h.

At the equator the plane of oscillation gets carried around with the rotation of the earth, following the changing direction of $\vec{g}$, but its orientation with respect to the ground does not change. Hence at this location $T = \infty$.

CHAPTER 17

17-3

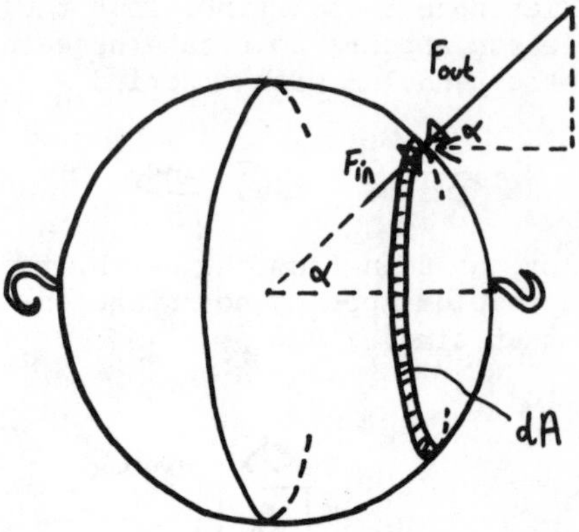

(a) The atmosphere pushes the hemispheres together while the air remaining inside tries to push them apart. We need to sum the components of these forces parallel to the forces exerted by the horses: that is, we want to sum

$$(F_{out} - F_{in}) \cos\alpha$$

over one hemisphere. This is

$$\int (P_{out} - P_{in}) dA \cos\alpha = \int P \cos\alpha \, dA.$$

Then the force that each team of horses must exert is

$$F = P \int \cos\alpha \, dA = 2\pi P \int_0^{\pi/2} R^2 \sin\alpha \cos\alpha \, d\alpha = \pi R^2 P \text{ \underline{Ans.}}$$

(b) Since $P_{atm} = 14.7 \text{ lb/in}^2$ we have

$$P = 14.70 - \frac{1}{10}(14.7) = 13.23 \text{ lb/in}^2 \rightarrow F = \pi (1 \text{ ft})^2 \frac{13.23 \text{ lb}}{(1/12 \text{ ft})^2}$$

$$F = 6000 \text{ lb \underline{Ans.}}$$

(c) Two teams of horses looks more impressive, but we could use one team and hook one hemisphere to the side of a building.

17-8

(a) The pressure variation in an isothermal atmosphere is

$$p = p_0 e^{-ay}.$$

At height $y = H$, $p = p_0/e$:

$$\frac{1}{e} p_0 = p_0 e^{-aH} \rightarrow -1 = -aH,$$

since $\ln e = 1$. But $a = g\rho_0/p_0$ so that

$$H = 1/a = p_0/\rho_0 g.$$

The pressure p_0 exerted at the base of an atmosphere of uniform density ρ_0 and height H is

$$p_0 = \rho_0 gH \rightarrow H = p_0/\rho_0 g,$$

the same as obtained above.

(b) Putting in numerical values from the text,

$$H = \frac{1}{a} = \frac{1}{0.116\ \text{km}^{-1}} = 8.6\ \text{km} \quad \underline{\text{Ans.}}$$

<u>17-12</u>

(a) The force exerted by the water against the shaded area is

$$dF_x = p_x dA = (\rho g x)W\,dx.$$

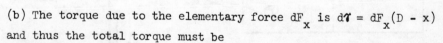

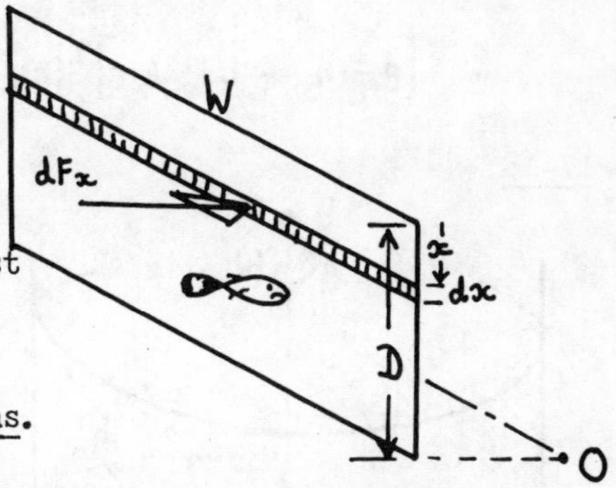

Therefore the force exerted against the entire face of the dam is

$$F = \int dF_x = \rho g W \int_0^D x\,dx = \frac{1}{2} g\rho W D^2 \quad \underline{\text{Ans.}}$$

(b) The torque due to the elementary force dF_x is $d\tau = dF_x(D - x)$ and thus the total torque must be

$$\tau = \int_0^D \rho g W x(D - x)dx = \rho g W\left(\frac{D^3}{2} - \frac{D^3}{3}\right) = \frac{1}{6} \rho g W D^3 \quad \underline{\text{Ans.}}$$

This gives only the horizontal component of the net torque.

(c) The line of action of $\vec{F}$ to give the same horizontal torque component as in (b) must be a distance d above the bottom of the dam where

$$F\,d = \tau \;\rightarrow\; \frac{1}{2}\,\rho g W D^2 d = \frac{1}{6}\,\rho g W D^3 \;\rightarrow\; d = \frac{1}{3}\,D \quad \underline{\text{Ans.}}$$

17-14

In effect, gravity takes a slab of fluid $\frac{1}{2}(h_2 - h_1)$ in thickness and lets it fall a distance $\frac{1}{2}(h_2 - h_1)$. Thus the work W done by gravity must be

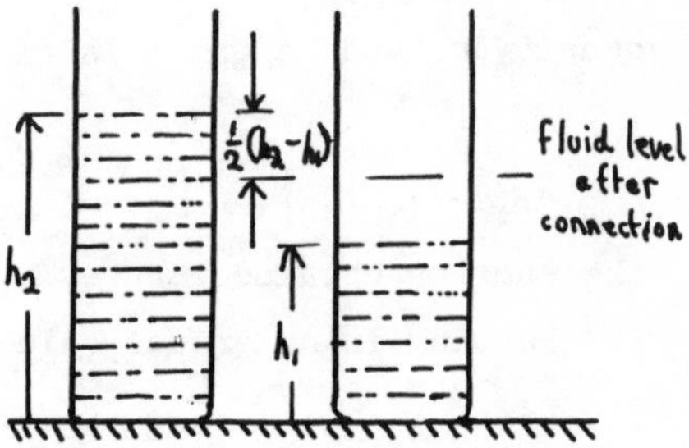

$$W = (\text{weight of slab})\,\frac{1}{2}(h_2 - h_1).$$

But the weight of the slab is just the weight density of the fluid times the volume of fluid moved. Therefore,

$$W = \left[\rho\,\frac{1}{2}(h_2 - h_1)\,A\,g\right]\frac{1}{2}(h_2 - h_1) = \frac{1}{4}\,\rho g A (h_2 - h_1)^2 \quad \underline{\text{Ans.}}$$

17-18

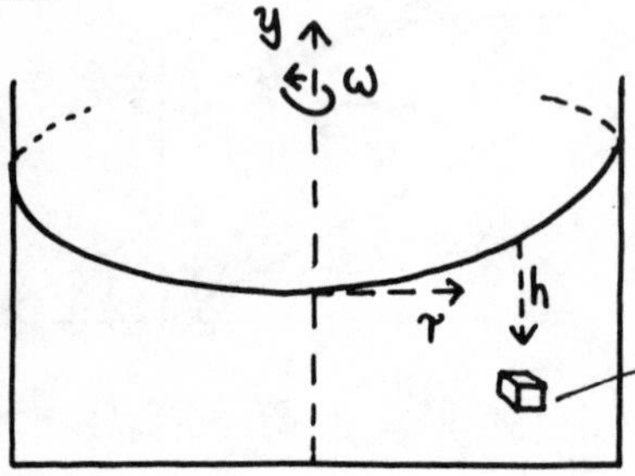

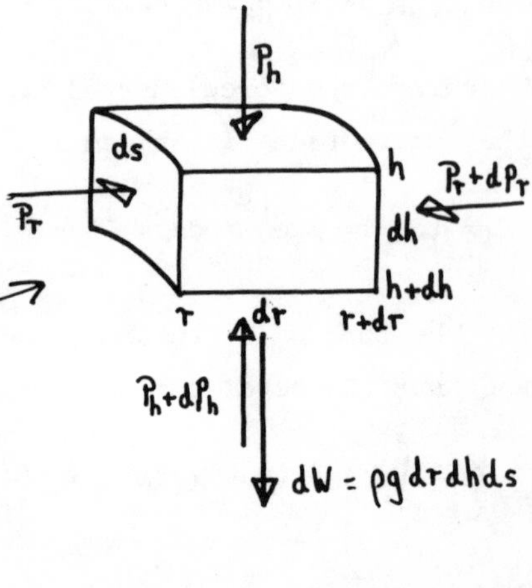

Consider conditions for equilibrium of the small element of fluid shown.

(a) In the radial (r) direction,

$$(ds\ dh)p_r - (p_r + dp_r)(ds\ dh) = -(dm)r\omega^2 = -(\rho\ ds\ dh\ dr)r\omega^2,$$

$$-dp_r\ ds\ dh = -\rho\ ds\ dh\ dr\ r\omega^2 \rightarrow dp_r/dr = \rho r\omega^2 \text{ \underline{Ans}.}$$

(b) Let the pressure on the axis of rotation r = 0 be $p(0) = p_c$; this will be a function of h. Integrating (a),

$$p_r = \frac{1}{2}\rho\omega^2 r^2 + p(0) = \frac{1}{2}\rho\omega^2 r^2 + p_c \text{ \underline{Ans}.}$$

(c) An element of fluid near the surface suffers a radial acceleration due to the rotation and will behave like the fluid in a tank under a horizontal acceleration. Then, from problem 17-16(a),

$$\tan\theta = a_r/g = \frac{\omega^2 r}{g} = \frac{dy}{dr} \rightarrow dy = \frac{\omega^2 r\ dr}{g} \rightarrow y = \frac{1}{2}\frac{\omega^2 r^2}{g} \text{ \underline{Ans},}$$

since, at the surface, r = 0 corresponds to y = 0.

(d) For equilibrium of the fluid element in the vertical direction,

$$p_h\ ds\ dr - (p_h + dp_h)ds\ dr + dW = 0.$$

But $dW = \rho g\ ds\ dh\ dr$ so we obtain

$$dp_h = \rho g\ dh \text{ \underline{Ans}.}$$

<u>17-21</u>

(a) For the minimum area A of ice we let the ice sink 1 ft so that the top surface of the ice is at the water line. The buoyant force must support the weight of the ice + car. The ice weighs

$$(0.92)(62.4\ \text{lb/ft}^3)(A)(1\ \text{ft})$$

and the car weighs 2500 lb. The buoyant force is the weight of water displaced and so equals

$$(62.4\ \text{lb/ft}^3)(A)(1\ \text{ft}).$$

Thus we must have

$$62.4\ A = 2500 + (0.92)(62.4)\ A,$$

$$A = 500\ \text{ft}^2\ \underline{\text{Ans.}}$$

(b) We place the car in the center of the ice, otherwise the ice will tilt and the resulting buoyant force will diminish since there is less ice in the water and therefore less water displaced.

17-26

The buoyant force on the shell is

$$\frac{4}{3}\pi R_o^{\,3}(\rho_w g) = \frac{4}{3}\pi(1\ \text{ft})^3(62.4\ \text{lb/ft}^3) = 261.4\ \text{lb},$$

R_o the inner radius of the shell and ρ_w the density of the water. This must equal the weight of the shell which is, if ρ_e is the density of iron and R_i the inside radius of the shell,

$$W = \frac{4}{3}\pi(R_o^{\,3} - R_i^{\,3})(\rho_e g) = \frac{4}{3}\pi(1^3 - R_i^{\,3})(7.80)(62.4)\ \text{lb}.$$

Setting this equal to the buoyant force above allows us to solve for R_i; we get $R_i = 0.955$ ft so that the inner diameter is 1.91 ft Ans.

17-28

(a) Let the cube have volume V and weight W. Then, floating in mercury alone,

$$W = \frac{1}{4} V\rho_m g.$$

In the mercury plus water,

$$f\ V\rho_m g + (1 - f)V\rho_w g = W = \frac{1}{4} V\rho_m g,$$

where f = fraction of volume of cube in mercury, ρ_m = density of mercury = $1.36 \times 10^4\ \text{kg/m}^3$, ρ_w = density of water = $10^3\ \text{kg/m}^3$. If we put the numbers into the equation above and solve for f we get

$$f = 0.19 \text{ Ans.}$$

(b) Only the volume V and weight W of the object enter the analysis in (a); hence, the shape is of no import and the answer is no. (We assume the body is everywhere convex as seen from the outside.)

17-30

(a) The forces on the log are its weight W acting down and the buoyant force F(x) acting up. Here x measures the vertical displacement of the log from equilibrium. Since a length L of the log is submerged when the log is in equilibrium we have

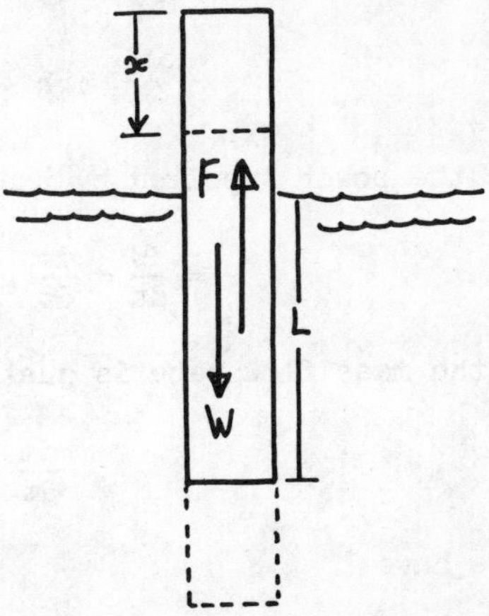

$$W = \rho_w gLA$$

where ρ_w is the density of water. When the log is displaced a distance x, Newton's second law gives

$$m\ddot{x} = \rho_w gLA - F(x) = \rho_w gLA - \rho_w gA(L + x),$$

$$m\ddot{x} = -\rho_w gAx \rightarrow (\rho_w LA)\ddot{x} = -\rho_w gAx,$$

$$\ddot{x} + \frac{g}{L}x = 0,$$

the last equation being that for simple harmonic motion.

(b) The period is

$$T = 2\pi\sqrt{\frac{L}{g}} = 2\pi\sqrt{\frac{8 \text{ ft}}{32 \text{ ft/s}^2}} = \pi = 3.1 \text{ s Ans.}$$

18-4

The work done by the pump on a mass m of water is

$$W = mgh + \frac{1}{2} mv^2.$$

Thus the power supplied by the pump is

$$P = \frac{dW}{dt} = \frac{dm}{dt}(gh + \frac{1}{2} v^2).$$

But the mass flow rate is just

$$\frac{dm}{dt} = Av\rho ,$$

so we have

$$P = Av\rho \, (gh + \frac{1}{2} v^2),$$

$$P = \pi(10^{-2} \text{ m})^2(5 \text{ m/s})(10^3 \text{ kg/m}^3) \left[(9.8 \text{ m/s}^2)(3 \text{ m}) + \frac{1}{2}(5 \text{ m/s})^2\right],$$

$$P = 66 \text{ W} \quad \underline{\text{Ans.}}$$

18-11

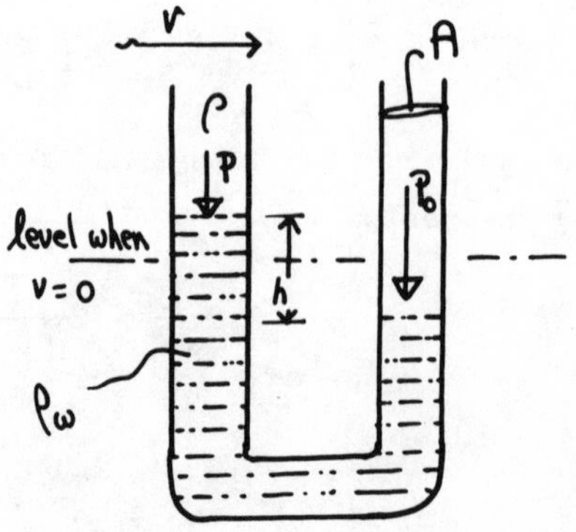

Let ρ be the density of air and ρ_w that of water. By Bernoulli's equation

$$p + \frac{1}{2}\rho v^2 = p_0,$$

the streamlines being horizontal. Thus the net force on the water column is

$$F = (p_0 - p)A = \text{weight of excess water} = (hA)\rho_w g,$$

which can be solved for h:

$$h = \tfrac{1}{2}\rho v^2 A/\rho_w gA,$$

$$h = \frac{(0.5)(1.2\ \text{kg/m}^3)(15\ \text{m/s})^2}{(10^3\text{kg/m}^3)(9.8\ \text{m/s}^2)} = 0.014\ \text{m} = 1.4\ \text{cm}\ \underline{\text{Ans.}}$$

18-12

(a) Note that if p_0 = atmospheric pressure, then $p_D = p_C = p_0$ and also that $v_D = 0$ approximately; then, applying Bernoulli's equation between points D and C gives

$$p_0 + 0 + 0 = p_0 + \tfrac{1}{2}\rho v^2 - \rho g(h_2 + d) \rightarrow v = \sqrt{2g(h_2 + d)}\ \underline{\text{Ans.}}$$

(b) By the equation of continuity, if the tube has a uniform cross-sectional area $v_B = v_C = v$. Then, by applying Bernoulli's equation between points D and B,

$$p_0 + 0 + 0 = p_B + \tfrac{1}{2}\rho v^2 + \rho g h_1 \rightarrow p_B = p_0 - \rho g(h_2 + d + h_1)\ \underline{\text{Ans.}}$$

(c) Clearly $p_B \geqslant 0$ so that $\rho g(h_2 + d + h_1) \leqslant p_0$. For maximum h_1 choose $h_2 + d = 0$; this gives

$$h_{1,max} = p_0/\rho g = 39\ \text{ft} = 10.3\ \text{m}\ \underline{\text{Ans.}}$$

18-18

Since streamlines 2 and 3 originate from streamline 1 it is reasonable that

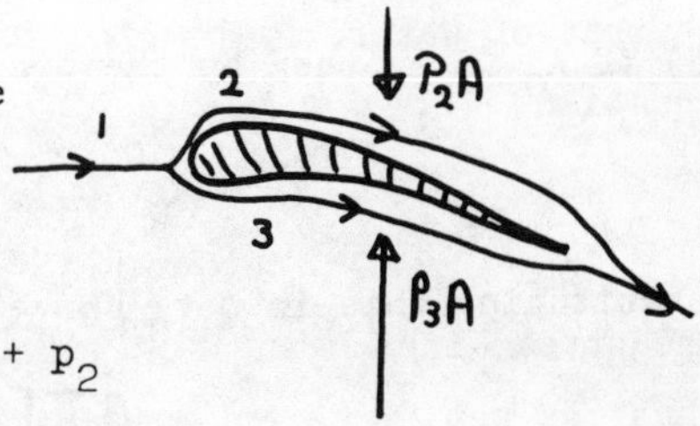

$$\tfrac{1}{2}\rho v_1^2 + \rho g y_1 + p_1 = \tfrac{1}{2}\rho v_2^2 + \rho g y_2 + p_2$$
$$= \tfrac{1}{2}\rho v_3^2 + \rho g y_3 + p_3.$$

For all practical purposes $y_1 = y_2 = y_3$ so that

$$\frac{1}{2}\rho v_2{}^2 + p_2 = \frac{1}{2}\rho v_3{}^2 + p_3,$$

and therefore

$$p_3 - p_2 = 20 \text{ lb/ft}^2 = \frac{1}{2}\rho(v_2{}^2 - v_3{}^3).$$

Let $\rho = 1.2 \text{ kg/m}^3 = 2.33 \times 10^{-3} \text{ slug/ft}^3$; we also have $v_3 = 350$ ft/s so that

$$v_2 = 374 \text{ ft/s} \quad \underline{\text{Ans.}}$$

<u>18-20</u>

Applying Bernoulli's equation between the top surface of the fluid and the opening,

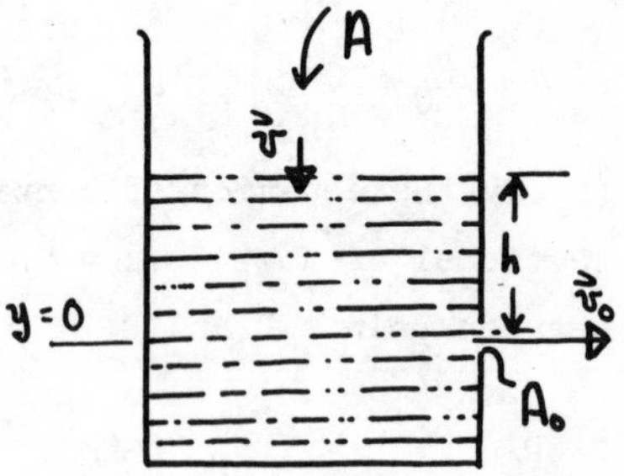

(a) $p_0 + \frac{1}{2}\rho v^2 + \rho gh = p_0 + \frac{1}{2}\rho v_0{}^2,$

$$v_0{}^2 = v^2 + 2gh.$$

(b) From the equation of continuity,

$$Av = A_0 v_0 \rightarrow v_0 = \frac{A}{A_0} v,$$

$$v_0 = (A/A_0)(v_0{}^2 - 2gh)^{1/2}.$$

Solving for v_0 gives

$$v_0 = \left[2gh/(1 - A_0{}^2/A^2)\right]^{1/2} \quad \underline{\text{Ans.}}$$

(c) If $A_0 \ll A$, then by the binomial expansion,

$$(1 - A_0{}^2/A^2)^{-1/2} = 1 + \frac{1}{2}(A_0/A)^2.$$

Substituting this into v_0 above yields

$$v_0 = \sqrt{2gh}\left[1 + \frac{1}{2}(A_0/A)^2\right] \quad \underline{\text{Ans.}}$$

18-21

Apply Bernoulli's equation to any streamline along the tube, between points 1 and 2:

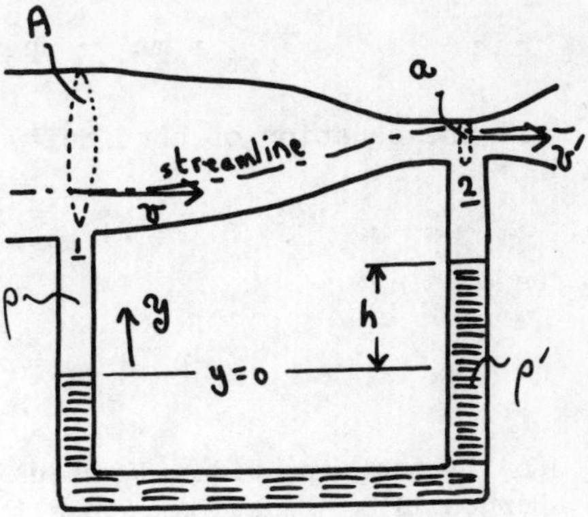

$$p_1 + \rho g y_1 + \frac{1}{2}\rho v^2 = p_2 + \rho g y_2 + \frac{1}{2}\rho v'^2.$$

By the continuity equation,

$$Av = av'$$

so that

$$p_1 + \rho g y_1 + \frac{1}{2}\rho v^2 = p_2 + \rho g y_2 + \frac{1}{2}\rho (A^2/a^2)v^2. \qquad (*)$$

Equating the pressures at $y = 0$ in the U-tube,

$$\rho g y_1 + p_1 = p_2 + \rho g(y_2 - h) + \rho' gh.$$

Eliminating $p_1 - p_2$ between this and (*) gives

$$\rho g y_2 - \rho g y_1 + \frac{1}{2}\rho v^2(A^2/a^2 - 1) = \rho g(y_2 - h) + \rho' gh - \rho g y_1.$$

The terms $\rho g(y_2 - y_1)$ cancel and the remaining expression may be solved for v:

$$v = a\sqrt{\frac{2(\rho' - \rho)\, gh}{\rho(A^2 - a^2)}} \quad \underline{\text{Ans.}}$$

18-24

It should be borne in mind that the analysis given here can be approximate only.

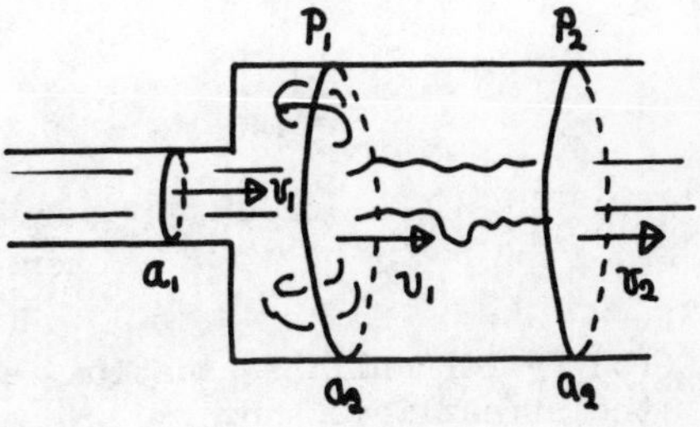

(a) Since the enlargement is abrupt the pressure p_1 still acts over the left area a_2 where the average fluid velocity is still $\vec{v}_1$. Then by the second law,

$$F_{ext} = ma \rightarrow p_2a_2 - p_1a_2 = \rho a_1v_1(v_1 - v_2),$$

and the equation of continuity

$$v_1a_1 = v_2a_2$$

we obtain

$$p_2 - p_1 = \rho v_2(v_1 - v_2) \ \underline{\text{Ans.}}$$

(b) If the pipe widened gradually (no turbulence) we could apply Bernoulli's equation: since the pipe is horizontal, presumeably,

$$p_1 + \frac{1}{2}\rho v_1^2 + \rho g y_1 = p_2' + \frac{1}{2}\rho v_2^2 + \rho g y_2,$$

$$p_2' - p_1 = \frac{1}{2}\rho(v_1^2 - v_2^2) \ \underline{\text{Ans,}}$$

where p_2' is the pressure at a_2 for a gradually widened pipe.

(c) From (a) and (b) the loss in pressure due to the abrupt enlargement is

$$p_2' - p_2 = \frac{1}{2}\rho(v_1^2 - v_2^2) - \rho v_2v_1 + \rho v_2^2 = \frac{1}{2}\rho(v_1 - v_2)^2 \ \underline{\text{Ans.}}$$

An analogy with elastic and inelastic collisions is probably not appropriate here since it is interaction between the fluid and the walls of the pipe which is of importance.

<u>18-28</u>

(a) Let outward directions be positive. Newton's second law tells us,

$$F = ma \rightarrow -(p + dp)A + pA = -(\rho A\ dr)\frac{v^2}{r},$$

$$\frac{dp}{dr} = \rho\frac{v^2}{r} \ \underline{\text{Ans.}}$$

(b) By Bernoulli's equation, assuming the constant is the same on the streamlines shown,

$$p + \frac{1}{2}\rho v^2 = (p + dp) + \frac{1}{2}\rho(v + dv)^2,$$

since the flow is horizontal.

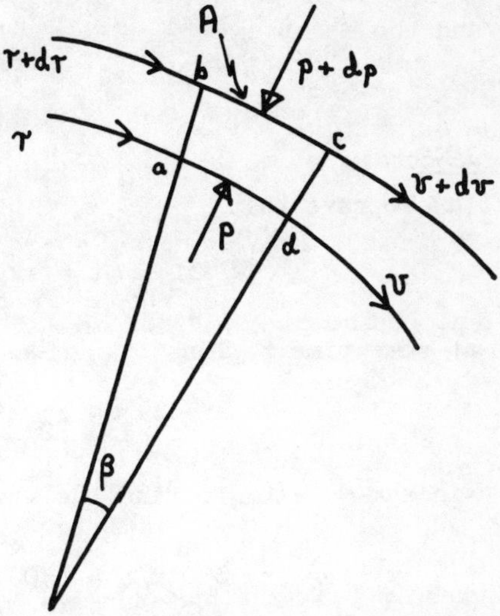

Letting $(dv)^2 \to 0$ we have

$$dp = -\ \rho v\ dv.$$

Invoking (a) gives

$$\rho\frac{v^2}{r}\ dr = -\rho v\ dv \ \to\ \frac{dr}{r} = -\frac{dv}{v}.$$

Integrating,

$$\ln r = -\ln v + C \ \to\ rv = \text{const.}$$

(c) From problem 18-26 we compute the line integral $\int \vec{v}\cdot\vec{ds}$. Choosing the path abcd shown and noting that $\vec{v} \perp \vec{ds}$ along $\widehat{ab}$ and $\widehat{cd}$ we find

$$\int_{abcd} \vec{v}\cdot\vec{ds} = \int_b^c \vec{v}\cdot\vec{ds} + \int_d^a \vec{v}\cdot\vec{ds} = (v + dv)(r + dr)\beta - rv\beta\ .$$

Allow $(dr)(dv) \to 0$ and use the result from (b). We then get

$$\int \vec{v}\cdot\vec{ds} = \beta(vr + r\ dv + v\ dr - vr) = \beta(r\ dv + v\ dr) = 0.$$

Since any closed path can be constructed from many small paths like that shown above we conclude that the flow is irrotational.

CHAPTER 19

19-5

(a) We have that

$$kx_1 - \omega t = kx_2 - \omega t + \pi/3$$

at some time t. Thus

$$x_1 - x_2 = \pi/3k = \lambda/6$$

since $k = 2\pi/\lambda$. To find the wavelength note that

$$v = \nu\lambda \rightarrow 350 \text{ m/s} = (500 \text{ s}^{-1})\lambda \rightarrow \lambda = \frac{7}{10} \text{ m.}$$

Therefore

$$x_1 - x_2 = (\frac{7}{10} \text{ m})/6 = \frac{7}{60} \text{ m} = 12 \text{ cm} \; \underline{\text{Ans.}}$$

(b) In this case

$$\Delta(\text{phase}) = (kx - \omega t_1) - (kx - \omega t_2)$$

$$= \omega(t_2 - t_1) = 2\pi\nu(t_2 - t_1)$$

$$= 2\pi(500 \text{ s}^{-1})(0.001 \text{ s}) = \pi \text{ rad} = 180° \; \underline{\text{Ans.}}$$

19-10

In general we may have

$$y = 5 \sin(kx - \omega t + \delta),$$

so that if at x = 10 cm,

$$y = 5 \sin(1.0 - 4.0 \text{ t})$$

then

(a) by direct comparison of the two equations

$$\omega = 4.0 \text{ rad/s} \rightarrow \nu = \frac{\omega}{2\pi} = 0.64 \text{ Hz } \underline{\text{Ans.}}$$

(b) The wavelength is

$$\lambda = v/\nu = (80 \text{ cm/s})/(0.64 \text{ s}^{-1}) = 125 \text{ cm } \underline{\text{Ans.}}$$

(c) By definition

$$k = 2\pi/\lambda = 2\pi/(125 \text{ cm}) = 0.050 \text{ cm}^{-1}.$$

Since $kx + \delta = 1$ at $x = 10$ cm,

$$(0.050 \text{ cm}^{-1})(10 \text{ cm}) + \delta = 1,$$

$$\delta = 0.50.$$

We conclude that the equation of the wave is

$$y = 5 \sin(0.05\ x - 4.0\ t + 0.50) \ \underline{\text{Ans.}},$$

x and y in cm, t in seconds.

(d) The tension is

$$T = \mu v^2 = (4 \text{ g/cm})(80 \text{ cm/s})^2 = 25600 \text{ dyne} = 0.26 \text{ N } \underline{\text{Ans.}}$$

19-14

(a) If T is the tension in the rope,

$$v(y) = \sqrt{\frac{T(y)}{\mu}}$$

where $\mu = m/L$. Consider a small element of the rope a distance y from the lower end ($y = 0$). The tension in that element is the weight of rope beneath it:

$$T = (\mu y)g.$$

Therefore

$$v = \sqrt{\frac{\mu y g}{\mu}} = \sqrt{yg} \ \underline{\text{Ans.}}$$

(b) Since $v = dy/dt$,

$$\sqrt{yg}\, dt = dy \rightarrow \sqrt{g}\, dt = y^{-1/2}\, dy.$$

If the wave starts at the bottom at $t = 0$ and reaches the top at $t = T$,

$$g^{1/2}(T - 0) = 2(L^{1/2} - 0^{1/2}) \rightarrow T = 2\sqrt{\frac{L}{g}} \text{ Ans.}$$

(c) The tension is due to the mass of the rope although the numerical value of m does not appear here.

19-18

(a) The particle displacement is $y = y_m \sin(kx \pm \omega t)$ and therefore for the particle velocity we have

$$\frac{\partial y}{\partial t} = u = \pm \omega y_m \cos(kx \pm \omega t) \rightarrow u_{max} = \omega y_m \text{ Ans.}$$

(b) The energy of an element of length Δx is

$$\frac{1}{2}(\mu \Delta x)^2 u_m{}^2 = \frac{1}{2}\mu \Delta x\, \omega^2 y_m{}^2 = 2\pi^2 \mu \Delta x\, \nu^2 y_m{}^2.$$

Thus the energy per unit length is just this energy divided by the length of the element Δx:

$$\text{energy per unit length} = 2\pi^2 \mu\, \nu^2 y_m{}^2 \text{ Ans.}$$

(c) The average power P is

$$P = \frac{\text{Energy/unit length}}{\text{time for wave to cross element}}.$$

Now the time in the denominator is just $t = \Delta x/v$ so that

$$P = (2\pi^2 \mu \Delta x\, \nu^2 y_m{}^2)/(\Delta x/v) = 2\pi^2 \mu \nu^2 y_m{}^2 v \text{ Ans.}$$

(d) These results hold as long as the individual particle motions are simple harmonic.

19-19

(a) Assuming no absorption the power crossing a sphere centered at the scource is independent of the sphere's radius. By definition of intensity this means that

$$4\pi\, r_1^{\,2} I_1 = 4\pi\, r_2^{\,2} I_2 = \text{constant.}$$

But the intensity I is proportional to the square of the amplitude A of the wave; thus also

$$4\pi\, r_1^{\,2} A_1^{\,2} = 4\pi\, r_2^{\,2} A_2^{\,2} = \text{constant}$$

where the constants in the two equations are different. We can write in general then

$$A = \frac{\text{constant}}{r} = Y/r$$

say. Let the scource be at $r = 0$ as we implied. Then the sinusoidal part of the displacement is

$$\sin(kr - \omega t) = \sin k(r - \frac{\omega}{k}\,t) = \sin k(r - vt)$$

giving

$$y = \frac{Y}{r}\sin k(r - vt)$$

regardless of direction since the wave is assumed to be uniform.

(b) The sine factor in the above is dimensionless. Since both y and r have dimensions of length, Y must have dimensions of the square of length.

19-24

With $\theta = kx - \omega t$ we can write the waves as

$$y_1 = A\sin\theta,$$

$$y_2 = \frac{A}{2}\sin(\theta + \frac{\pi}{2}) = \frac{A}{2}\cos\theta,$$

$$y_3 = \frac{A}{3}\sin(\theta + \pi) = -\frac{A}{3}\sin\theta,$$

since, if the periods are equal, the frequencies are equal. Then

$$y_T = y_1 + y_2 + y_3 = \frac{2A}{3}\sin\theta + \frac{A}{2}\cos\theta = \frac{2A}{3}(\sin\theta + \frac{3}{4}\cos\theta).$$

Let

$$\left.\begin{aligned}\alpha \sin\beta &= 1\\ \alpha \cos\beta &= 3/4\end{aligned}\right\} \alpha = 5/4,\ \tan\beta = 4/3.$$

Now we can express the resulting waveform y_T in terms of α and β:

$$y_T = \frac{5\ A}{6}\sin(\theta + \beta).$$

The graph is a simple sine wave with amplitude $\frac{5A}{6}$ and phase angle β, the frequency being the same as for the component waves. At $\theta = kx - \omega t = 0$,

$$y_T = \frac{5A}{6}\sin\beta = \frac{5A}{6}\sin(\tan^{-1}4/3)$$
$$= \frac{2\ A}{3}.$$

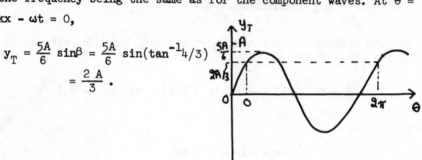

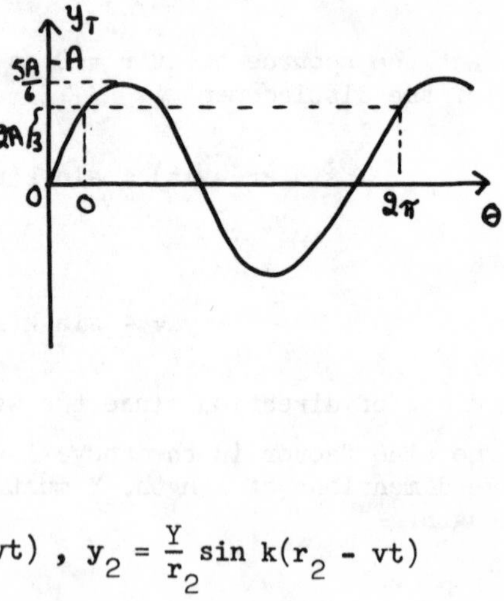

19-25

(a) We have two spherical waves,

$$y_1 = \frac{Y}{r_1}\sin k(r_1 - vt)\ ,\ y_2 = \frac{Y}{r_2}\sin k(r_2 - vt)$$

so that the resultant is

$$y = y_1 + y_2 = Y\left[\frac{\sin k(r_1 - vt)}{r_1} + \frac{\sin k(r_2 - vt)}{r_2}\right].$$

Now let

$$r_1 = r - \delta = r(1 - \frac{\delta}{r}),$$
$$r_2 = r + \delta = r(1 + \frac{\delta}{r}),$$

so that

$$r = \frac{1}{2}(r_2 + r_1), \quad \delta = \frac{1}{2}(r_2 - r_1).$$

In order that we be considering points at which r_1 is nearly equal to r_2 we need $\delta/r \ll 1$. We obtain

$$y \cong \frac{Y}{r}\left[(1 + \frac{\delta}{r}) \sin k(r_1 - vt) + (1 - \frac{\delta}{r}) \sin k(r_2 - vt)\right],$$

$$= \frac{Y}{r}\left[\sin k(r_1 - vt) + \sin k(r_2 - vt)\right]$$

$$+ \frac{Y}{r}\frac{\delta}{r}\left[\sin k(r_1 - vt) - \sin k(r_2 - vt)\right],$$

$$= \frac{Y}{r}\left[2 \sin \frac{k}{2}(r_1 + r_2 - 2vt) \cos \frac{k}{2}(r_1 - r_2)\right]$$

$$+ \frac{Y}{r}\frac{\delta}{r}\left[2 \sin \frac{k}{2}(r_1 - r_2) \cos \frac{k}{2}(r_1 + r_2 - 2vt)\right]$$

$$= 2\frac{Y}{r}\left[\sin k(r - vt) \cos k\delta - (\frac{\delta}{r}) \sin k\delta \cos k(r - vt)\right],$$

$$y \cong 2\frac{Y}{r} \cos k \frac{1}{2}(r_1 - r_2) \sin k(r - vt)$$

again since $\delta/r \ll 1$. This is a traveling wave with the amplitude being the coefficient of $\sin k(r - vt)$.

(b) For the amplitude to be zero we require $\cos \frac{k}{2}(r_1 - r_2)$ to be zero. But $k = 2\pi/\lambda$ so the condition is

$$\frac{\pi}{\lambda}(r_1 - r_2) = (n + \frac{1}{2})\pi, \; n = 0, 1, \ldots,$$

$$r_1 - r_2 = (n + \frac{1}{2})\lambda.$$

For total reinforcement,

$$\cos \frac{k}{2}(r_1 - r_2) = 1 \rightarrow \frac{\pi}{\lambda}(r_1 - r_2) = n\pi \rightarrow r_1 - r_2 = n\lambda,$$

where again n is zero or a positive integer.

19-27

(a) If $y_1 = y_m \sin(kx - \omega t)$ and $y_2 = y_m \sin(kx + \omega t)$ then

$$y = y_1 + y_2 = 2y_m \sin kx \cos \omega t = (0.5) \sin \tfrac{\pi}{3}x \cos 40\pi\ t.$$

Therefore the amplitudes are

$$y_m = (0.50\ \text{cm})/2 = 0.25\ \text{cm}\ \underline{\text{Ans}},$$

and

$$v = \frac{\omega}{k} = \frac{40\ \pi\ \text{rad/s}}{\pi/3\ \text{cm}^{-1}} = 120\ \text{cm/s}\ \underline{\text{Ans}}.$$

(b) The required distance is $\lambda/2$. But

$$\lambda = 2\pi/k = 2\pi/(\pi/3\ \text{cm}^{-1}) = 6\ \text{cm}$$

and therefore the distance between nodes is 3 cm Ans.

(c) The particle velocity is

$$u = \partial y/\partial t = -\ 20\pi\ \sin(\pi x/3)\ \sin(40\pi t)$$

for any x and t. The velocity at x = 1.5 cm, t = 9/8 s is

$$u = -\ 20\pi\ \sin(\pi/2)\ \sin(45\pi) = -\ 20\pi\ (+1)(0) = 0\ \underline{\text{Ans}}.$$

19-31

Associated with a length dx is kinetic energy dK and potential energy dU. The first of these is

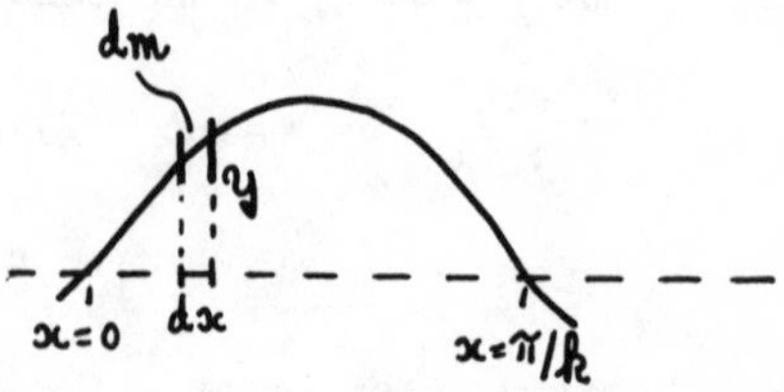

$$dK = \tfrac{1}{2}(dm)u^2 = \tfrac{1}{2}(\mu\, dx)u^2$$

where u is the speed of the element. From the equation of a standing wave this speed is

$$u = \partial y/\partial t = -\ 2\ y_m \omega \sin(kx)\sin(\omega t),$$

so that

$$dK = 2\mu\omega^2 y_m{}^2 \sin^2 kx\ \sin^2 \omega t\ dx.$$

The potential energy is that of a simple harmonic oscillator of dm; if a is the force constant then

$$dU = \frac{1}{2} ay^2$$

where

$$a = (dm)\omega^2 = \mu\omega^2 dx.$$

Hence

$$dU = \frac{1}{2}\mu\omega^2 y^2 dx = 2\mu\omega^2 y_m{}^2 \sin^2 kx \cos^2 \omega t \; dx.$$

Adding to get the total energy,

$$dU + dK = dE = 2\mu\omega^2 y_m{}^2 \sin^2 kx \; dx,$$

and integrating over one loop, substituting $\omega = vk = 2\pi\nu$,

$$E = 2\mu\omega^2 y_m{}^2 \int_0^{\pi/k} \sin^2 kx \; dx = 2\pi^2 \mu \, y_m{}^2 \nu v \;\; \underline{\text{Ans.}}$$

19-34

(a) From the tension T in the wire,

$$T = mg = (10 \text{ kg})(9.8 \text{ m/s}^2) = 98 \text{ N},$$

we find the wave velocities in the two pieces:

$$v_1 = \sqrt{T/\mu_1}\,, \; v_2 = \sqrt{T/\mu_2}.$$

Since μ is the mass per unit length we have

$$\mu = \rho AL/L = \rho A$$

where A is the cross-sectional area of the wire and ρ is the density of the wire. Thus we obtain

$$\mu_1 = (2.6 \text{ g/cm}^3)(10^{-2} \text{ cm}^2) = 2.6 \times 10^{-3} \text{ kg/m},$$

$$\mu_2 = (7.8 \text{ g/cm}^3)(10^{-2} \text{ cm}^2) = 7.8 \times 10^{-3} \text{ kg/m}.$$

These give for the wave speeds $v_1 = 194.1$ m/s and $v_2 = 112.1$ m/s.

The distance between adjacent nodes is $\lambda/2$ so that if we require that the joint be a node,

$$n_1\lambda_1/2 = L_1, \; n_2\lambda_2/2 = L_2.$$

It is given that $L_1 = 0.6$ m and $L_2 = 0.866$ m and therefore

$$n_1 = 0.00618\ \nu_1 \; , \; n_2 = 0.0155\ \nu_2.$$

Various possibilities are

n_1	$\nu_1(s^{-1})$	n_2	$\nu_2(s^{-1})$
1	162	1	65
2	324 ←	2	129
		3	194
		4	258
		5	323 ←

It appears that the sought-for frequency is 323 Hz Ans.

(b) We have 5 + 2 = 7 loops → 8 nodes - 2 at ends = 6 nodes Ans.

CHAPTER 20

20-9

The time t_1 for a stone to fall to the bottom of a well of depth d is

$$t_1 = \sqrt{\frac{2\,d}{g}}\,,$$

whilst the time t_2 for sound, traveling with speed v, to cover the same distance d is just

$$t_2 = d/v.$$

Hence the total time t that elapses between dropping the stone and hearing the splash is $t_1 + t_2$:

$$t = \sqrt{\frac{2\,d}{g}} + \frac{d}{v}\,.$$

We may solve this equation for d in terms of t; one finds

$$g\,d^2 - d(2v)(gt + v) + (vt)^2 g = 0 \;\rightarrow\; d = v\left[\left(\frac{v}{g} + t\right) \pm \sqrt{\left(\frac{v}{g}\right)\left(\frac{v}{g} + 2t\right)}\right].$$

The negative sign is appropriate since we want t = 0 to give d = 0. Putting in $g = 9.8\ \mathrm{m/s^2}$ and v = 331 m/s we find d = 41 m for t = 3 seconds Ans.

20-12

(a) The path difference between the two waves going via SBD must half a wavelength:

$$\frac{1}{2}\lambda = 2(1.65\ \mathrm{cm}) \;\rightarrow\; \lambda = 0.066\ \mathrm{m}\ \text{Ans.}$$

(b) Let A be the amplitude of the wave going route SAD and B the amplitude of the wave going via SBD in either position (we assume these last are equal). Since the intensity of a wave is proportional to the square of the amplitude we can write

$$\left.\begin{aligned}(A + B)^2 &= 900\\ (A - B)^2 &= 100\end{aligned}\right\} \rightarrow A = 20,\ B = 10 \text{ units.}$$

Thus $B/A = \frac{1}{2}$ Ans.

(c) The waves going SAD and SBD travel different distances and therefore lose different amount of energy through various dissipative processes.

20-13

Assuming that the angle of incidence equals the angle of reflection,

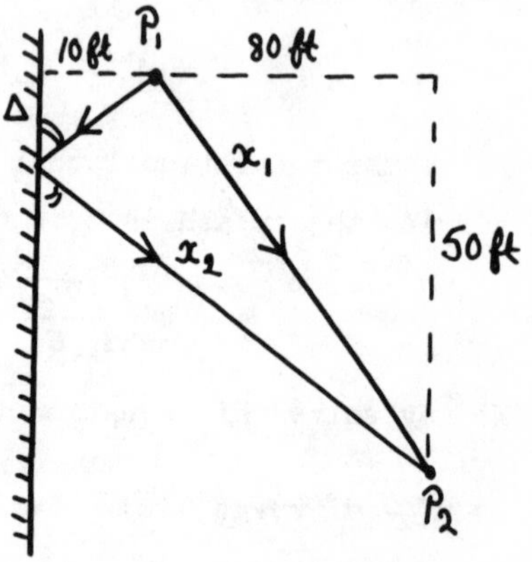

$$\frac{90}{50 - \Delta} = \frac{10}{\Delta} \rightarrow \Delta = 5 \text{ ft.}$$

The total path lengths are then

$$x_1 = \sqrt{80^2 + 50^2} = 94.3 \text{ ft,}$$

$$x_2 = \sqrt{10^2 + 5^2} + \sqrt{45^2 + 90^2},$$

$$x_2 = 111.8 \text{ ft.}$$

Thus the path difference is 17.5 ft. For constructive interference we want this to equal an integral number of half-wavelengths, there being a phase change of 180° upon reflection. Therefore

$$(n + \tfrac{1}{2})\lambda = 17.5 \text{ ft.}$$

(i) $n = 0$: $\lambda = 35$ ft, $\nu_0 = (1100 \text{ ft/s})/(35 \text{ ft}) = 31$ Hz Ans,

(ii) $n = 1$: $\lambda = 11.7$ ft, $\nu_1 = (1100 \text{ ft/s})/(11.7 \text{ ft}) = 94$ Hz Ans.

20-19

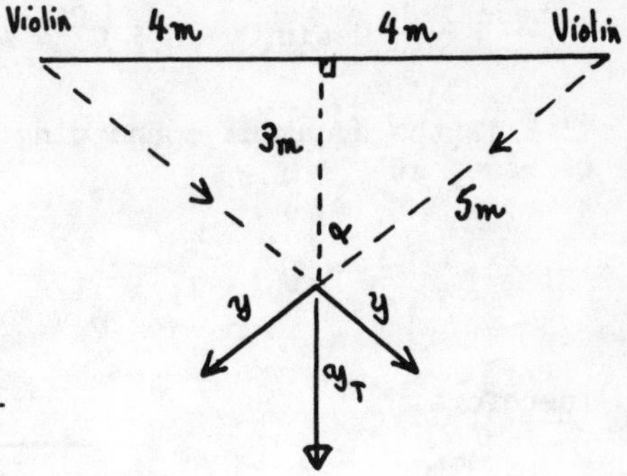

(a) The intensity of either wave at a distance of 5 m is

$$I = \frac{S}{4\pi r^2} = \frac{10^{-4}\ W}{4\pi(5\ m)^2},$$

$$I = 3.2 \times 10^{-7}\ W/m^2 \ \underline{Ans.}$$

(b) The intensity is proportional to the square of the resultant amplitude. If y is the amplitude of either wave at the conductor, the resultant amplitude will be

$$y_r = 2y \cos\alpha = 2y(\tfrac{3}{5}) = \tfrac{6}{5}\, y.$$

Squaring gives for the resultant intensity

$$I_r = \frac{36}{25} I = 4.6 \times 10^{-7}\ W/m^2 \ \underline{Ans.}$$

We have taken it for granted that the violinists are playing in phase.

20-20

(a) The wavelength of the sound is

$$\lambda = c/\nu = (330\ m/s)/(200\ s^{-1}) = 1.65\ m,$$

and therefore we have for the path difference,

$$\text{path difference} = 4\ m - 3\ m = 0.606\lambda\ .$$

This corressponds to a phase difference = $(0.606)(2\pi) = 218°$. However the waves arrive from opposite directions so the actual phase difference is $218° - 180° = 38° = \beta$. We assumed the scources are in phase Ans.

If $\alpha = \omega t$ then the displacement at P is

$$y = A_1 \sin\alpha + A_2 \sin(\alpha + \beta) = (A_1 + A_2\cos\beta)\sin\alpha + A_2 \sin\beta \cos\alpha.$$

This can be written in the alternate form

$$y = C\sin(\alpha + \delta),\quad C^2 = A_1^{\,2} + 2A_1A_2\cos\beta + A_2^{\,2}.$$

If k is the constant connecting intensity with amplitude squared, we have, at P,

$$I = kC^2,\quad I_1 = kA_1^{\,2} = \frac{S_1}{4\pi r_1^{\,2}},\quad I_2 = \frac{S_2}{4\pi r_2^{\,2}}.$$

Therefore

$$I = \frac{S_1}{4\pi\, r_1^{\,2}} + 2\sqrt{\frac{S_1}{4\pi\, r_1^{\,2}}\,\frac{S_2}{4\pi\, r_2^{\,2}}}\,\cos\beta + \frac{S_2}{4\pi\, r_2^{\,2}}.$$

We have $S_1 = 1.2 \times 10^{-3}$ W, $r_1 = 4$ m, $S_2 = 1.8 \times 10^{-3}$ W, $r_2 = 3$ m, $\beta = 38°$. Carrying out the numerical work yields

(b) $S_1/4\pi r_1^{\,2} = 6.0 \times 10^{-6}$ W/m^2 Ans;

(c) $S_2/4\pi r_2^{\,2} = 16 \times 10^{-6}$ W/m^2 Ans;

(d) $I = 37 \times 10^{-6}$ W/m^2 Ans.

20-26

(a) In the fundamental mode

$$L = \lambda_0/2 = \frac{v}{2\nu_0}.$$

If x is the length the string is shortened,

$$L - x = v/(2\,r\nu_0).$$

Elimination of ν_0 between these equations gives

$$x = L\left(1 - \frac{1}{r}\right) \text{ Ans.}$$

(b) For L = 80 cm we get by successive substitution of r = 6/5, 5/4, 4/3, 3/2 these values of x: 13, 16, 20, 27 cm respectively Ans.

20-30

(a) The center of the star must be a displacement node Ans.

(b) In the fundamental mode of oscillation we have antinodes at the surface and nowhere else. Since the distance between antinodes is one-half the wavelength we have, putting v_s/ν for the wavelength,

$$\frac{1}{2}(v_s/\nu) = 2\ R \ \rightarrow\ T = 4\ R/v_s \ \text{Ans},$$

since $\nu = 1/T$.

(c) The speed of sound is

$$v_s = \sqrt{\frac{\gamma P}{\rho}} = \sqrt{\frac{(4/3)(10^{22}\ \text{Pa})}{10^{10}\ \text{kg/m}^3}} = 1.15 \times 10^6\ \text{m/s},$$

and we have for the radius R of the star

$$R = (0.009)(7 \times 10^8\ \text{m}) = 6.3 \times 10^6\ \text{m}.$$

Substituting these into (b) gives T = 22 s for the pulsation period Ans.

20-32

Possible frequencies are

$$\frac{v}{2\ L},\ \frac{v}{L},\ \frac{3\ v}{2\ L}\ \text{etc.},$$

among which are 880, 1320 Hz as consecutive frequencies. But 880/1320 = 2/3 and therefore

$$880\ \text{Hz} = \frac{v}{L},\ 1320\ \text{Hz} = \frac{3}{2}\frac{v}{L}.$$

Either expression gives

$$v = (880)(L) = (880\ \text{s}^{-1})(0.316\ \text{m}) = 278\ \text{m/s} = \sqrt{T/(6.5 \times 10^{-4}\ \text{kg/m}},$$

$$T = 50\ \text{N Ans}.$$

20-33

In the fundamental mode we have

$$\lambda = 2L = \frac{v}{\nu} \rightarrow \nu = \frac{1}{2L}\sqrt{\frac{T}{\mu}} .$$

To obtain 6 beats we need to change the frequency of one wire by 6 Hz. Take differentials of the last equation and divide the result by the equation itself to get

$$\frac{\Delta\nu}{\nu} = \frac{1}{2}\frac{\Delta T}{T} .$$

Since $\Delta\nu/\nu = 0.01$ we find $\Delta T/T = 2\%$ Ans.

20-38

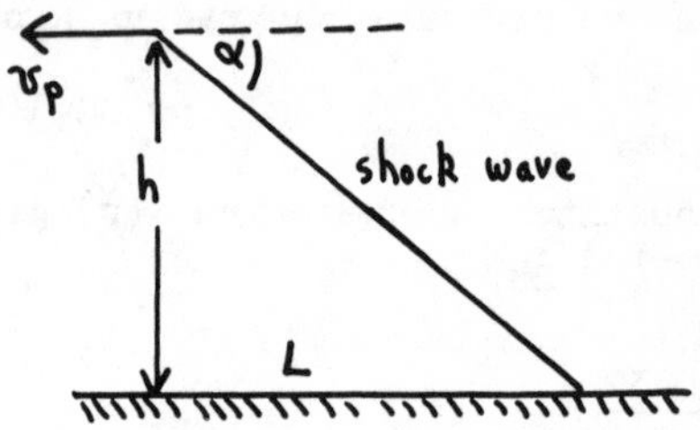

(a) Let v_p be the speed of the jet. Then the half-angle α of the shock cone is given by

$$\sin\alpha = v/v_p = v/1.5\ v = 2/3,$$

$$\alpha = 42° \text{ Ans.}$$

(b) The shock travels with the plane at a speed 1.5(331 m/s) = 496.5 m/s. It must cover a distance $L = h \cot\alpha = (5000\text{ m})(1.117)$ = 5585 m to reach the ground observer. Clearly it will take

$$t = (5585\text{ m})/(496.5\text{ m/s}) = 11\text{ s Ans.}$$

20-42

(a) The wavelength is (1080 ft/s)/(1080 Hz) = 1.0 ft Ans.

(b) Let ν' be the frequency of the sound as seen by the surface;

$$\nu' = \nu\left(\frac{v + v_o}{v - v_s}\right) = (1080\ s^{-1})\ \frac{1080 + 216}{1080 - 108} = 1440\text{ Hz Ans.}$$

(c) The speed of the reflected sound waves with respect to the still air is 1080 ft/s Ans.

(d) The wavelength λ' of the reflected waves is just

$$\lambda' = v/\nu' = (1080 \text{ ft/s})/(1440 \text{ Hz}) = 0.75 \text{ ft } \underline{\text{Ans.}}$$

20-44

Since the plane sees an approaching scource the frequency ν' at which it receives signals is

$$\nu' = \nu(1 + \frac{u}{c})$$

where ν is the rest frequency of the scource. The receiver also sees an approaching scource (the plane) and it receives the reflected microwaves as at a frequency ν'' given by

$$\nu'' = \nu'(1 + \frac{u}{c}) = \nu(1 + \frac{u}{c})^2.$$

Since $\frac{u}{c} \ll 1$ for today's planes

$$\nu'' = \nu(1 + 2\frac{u}{c}) \rightarrow \frac{\nu'' - \nu}{\nu} = 2\frac{u}{c}.$$

But $\nu = c/\lambda$ so we have

$$u = \frac{\lambda}{2}(\nu'' - \nu) = \frac{1}{2}(0.10 \text{ m})(990 \text{ s}^{-1}) = 49.5 \text{ m/s } \underline{\text{Ans.}}$$

20-47

(a) The frequency the uncle hears is

$$\nu' = \nu(\frac{v}{v + v_s}) = (500 \text{ Hz}) \frac{331}{331 + 10} = 485 \text{ Hz } \underline{\text{Ans.}}$$

(b) Since the relative velocity between the girl and the train is zero she hears the rest frequency of the whistle = 500 Hz Ans.

(c) We need velocities relative to the medium, i.e. the air. The train moves 20 m/s and the uncle 10 m/s relative to the air, both to the east. Since they are moving apart

$$\nu' = (500 \text{ Hz}) \frac{331 + 10}{331 + 20} = 486 \text{ Hz } \underline{\text{Ans.}}$$

(d) The girl is still at rest relative to the train: 500 Hz Ans.

CHAPTER 21

21-2

(a) The cooling of an object can occur by radiation, conduction, evaporation, etc. and these will be affected by the nature of the material, its surface area and temperature, the temperature of the surroundings, the presence or absence of air currents, the vapor pressure of evaporated gas, etc.
The units in the equation

$$\frac{d\,\Delta T}{dt} = -K\,\Delta T$$

are

$$\text{kelvins/seconds} = K\,(\text{kelvins});$$

therefore the units of K must be $(\text{seconds})^{-1}$, that is $(\text{time})^{-1}$.

(b) Rearrange the expression of Newton's law of cooling and then integrate:

$$\frac{d\,\Delta T}{dt} = -K\,\Delta T \rightarrow \frac{d\,\Delta T}{\Delta T} = -K\,dt \rightarrow \Delta T = C\,e^{-Kt}$$

where C is a constant. To evaluate it put $t = 0$ and $\Delta T = \Delta T_0$; one finds that $C = \Delta T_0$. Therefore we have

$$\Delta T = \Delta T_0 e^{-Kt} \quad \underline{\text{Ans.}}$$

21-7

(a) Since

$$T_F = 32°F + \frac{9}{5}T_C$$

we set $T_F = T_C = T$. This gives

$$T = 32°F + \frac{9}{5}T \rightarrow T = -40° \quad \underline{\text{Ans.}}$$

(b) The relation between the Kelvin and Fahrenheit scales is

$$T_C = T_K - 273.15 = \frac{5}{9}T_F - 17.78.$$

Set $T_K = T_F = T$:

$$T - 273.15 = \frac{5}{9}T - 17.78 \rightarrow T = 575^\circ \text{ \underline{Ans}.}$$

(c) The Kelvin and Celsius scales are identical except for the choice of the zero point. Therefore they can never be equal but always differ by the difference in their zero points.

21-14

The area of the plate is A = a b before heating, but after the temperature rises the new area will be

$$A + \Delta A = (a + \Delta a)(b + \Delta b).$$

But this may be written

$$A + \Delta A = a(1 + \frac{\Delta a}{a})\cdot b(1 + \frac{\Delta b}{b}) = ab(1 + \frac{\Delta a}{a} + \frac{\Delta b}{b})$$

if $\Delta a/a$, $\Delta b/b \ll 1$ for then the product of these quantities is of second order. But $\Delta a = \alpha\, a\Delta T$ and $\Delta b = \alpha\, b\Delta T$ so we have

$$A + \Delta A = A(1 + 2\alpha\,\Delta T) \rightarrow \Delta A = 2\alpha\, A\,\Delta T \text{ \underline{Ans}.}$$

21-22

We know that the volume of mercury increases by $\beta V_0 t$ and the volume of the bulb increases by $3\alpha V_0 t$ approximately. Hence a volume

$$(\beta - 3\alpha)V_0 t$$

of mercury must leave the bulb. This enters the capillary and if it reaches a height h it will occupy a volume $A_0 h$. Therefore

$$A_0 h = (\beta - 3\alpha)V_0 t \rightarrow h = \frac{V_0}{A_0}(\beta - 3\alpha)t \text{ \underline{Ans}.}$$

21-26

(a) The angular momentum is

$$L = I\omega = \frac{1}{2} MR^2\omega = \frac{1}{2}(0.5 \text{ kg})(0.03 \text{ m})^2(60 \text{ rad/s}) = 0.0135 \text{ kg}\cdot\text{m}^2/\text{s}.$$

From the work-energy theorem,

$$W = \frac{1}{2}(\frac{1}{2} MR^2)\omega^2 = 0.405 \text{ J } \underline{\text{Ans.}}$$

We can assume that no torques act on the cylinder during heating and therefore

$$\Delta L = 0 \cong I\ \Delta\omega + \omega\ \Delta I$$

so that

$$\frac{\Delta\omega}{\omega} = -\frac{\Delta I}{I} = -2\ \alpha\ \Delta T$$

by problem 21-25. By these arguements we conclude that

(b)

$$\frac{\Delta\omega}{\omega} = -2(2 \times 10^{-5}\ /C°)(80\ C°) = -0.32\% \ \underline{\text{Ans}},$$

(c)

$$\frac{\Delta L}{L} = 0.00\% \ \underline{\text{Ans.}}$$

(d) The change ΔK in the kinetic energy $K = \frac{1}{2} I\omega^2$ will satisfy

$$\frac{\Delta K}{K} = \frac{\Delta I}{I} + 2\frac{\Delta\omega}{\omega} = \frac{\Delta\omega}{\omega} = -0.32\% \ \underline{\text{Ans.}}$$

21-28

If h be the vertical distance of C below the points of support we want $\Delta h = 0$, i.e.,

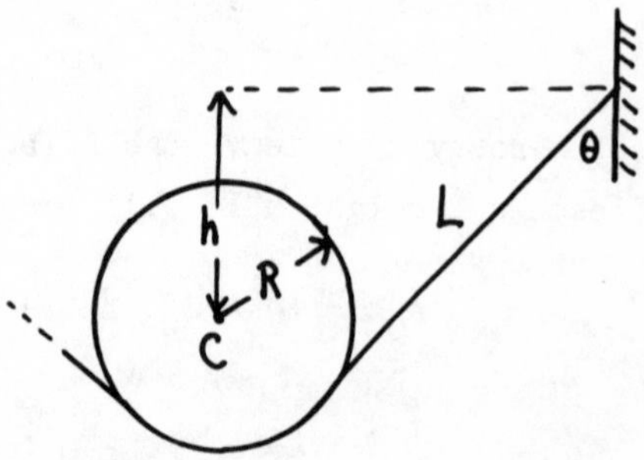

$$\Delta h = 0 = (\Delta L)\cos\theta - \Delta R,$$

$$(\alpha_s L\ \Delta T)\cos\theta = \alpha_{al} R\ \Delta T,$$

$$R = \frac{\alpha_s}{\alpha_{al}} L \cos\theta = \frac{11 \times 10^{-6} /C^\circ}{23 \times 10^{-6} /C^\circ}(2.5 \text{ m})(\cos 50^\circ),$$

$$R = 77 \text{ cm } \underline{\text{Ans}}.$$

<u>21-30</u>

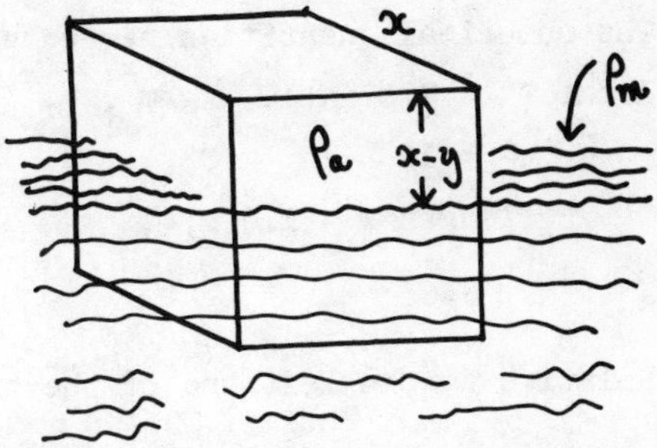

The weight of the cube is $x^3 \rho_a g$. Before heating we have a buoyant force of $x^2 y \rho_m g$. Thus

$$x^2 y \rho_m g = x^3 \rho_a g \rightarrow y\rho_m = x\rho_a.$$

All quantities in the last equation change on heating the system:

$$(y\ \delta\rho_m + \delta y\ \rho_m) = (\delta x\ \rho_a + \delta\rho_a\ x).$$

But the mass M of the cube remains constant:

$$M = x^3 \rho_a \rightarrow \Delta M = 0 = 3x^2 \delta x\ \rho_a + x^3 \delta\rho_a \rightarrow x\ \delta\rho_a = -\ 3\ \rho_a \delta x.$$

Therefore

$$(y\ \delta\rho_m + \delta y\ \rho_m) = -\ 2\rho_a \delta x.$$

Now if β is the coefficient of volume expansion of mercury then $\delta\rho_m = -\ \beta\ \rho_m \Delta T$ (problem 21-19); we substitute this into the equation above and solve for δy to obtain

$$\delta y = (\beta\ y - 2\frac{\rho_a}{\rho_m}\alpha\ x)\Delta T = (\beta - 2\ \alpha)\ x\ \frac{\rho_a}{\rho_m}\ \Delta T.$$

Taking numerical values from the tables and the statement of the problem we find $\delta y = 0.27$ mm <u>Ans</u>.

21-32

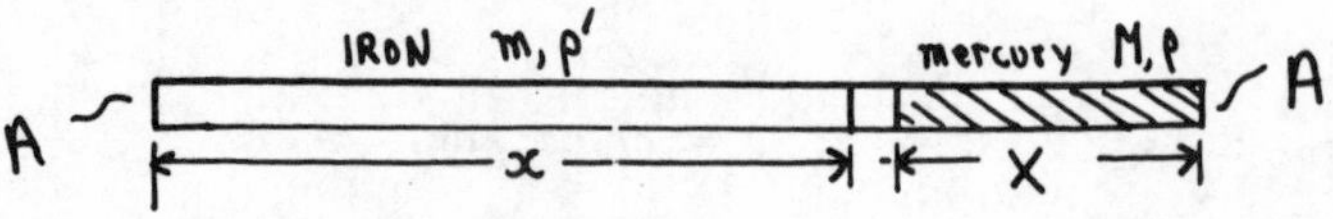

The numerical quantities needed are

Iron: $\rho' = 7.87 \times 10^3$ kg/m^3, $\alpha = 12 \times 10^{-6}$ /C°, length $x = 1.0$ m;

Mercury: $\rho = 13.6 \times 10^3$ kg/m^3, $\beta = 1 \times 10^{-}$ /C°;

Glass: mass = 0, $\alpha_g = 9 \times 10^{-6}$ /C°.

Relative to the left end of the tube the center of mass is given by

$$(m + M)x_{cm} = m(x/2) + M(x + X/2)$$

neglecting the glass. On heating the center of mass will move by an amount found from

$$(m + M)\Delta x_{cm} = m(\Delta x/2) + M(\Delta x - \Delta X/2),$$

$$m\,\Delta x + 2\,M\,\Delta x - M\,\Delta X = 0$$

if $\Delta x_{cm} = 0$. The changes in length are

$$\Delta X = (\beta - 2\alpha_g)X\,\Delta T = \beta^* X\,\Delta T,\quad \Delta x = \alpha\,x\,\Delta T$$

the former result from problem 21-27. Substituting these gives

$$m\alpha\,x + 2M\,\alpha x - M\,\beta^* X = 0.$$

But $M = XA\rho$ and $m = xA\rho'$. Insert these to find that

$$(\rho\beta^*)X^2 - (2\rho\,\alpha x)X - \rho'\alpha x^2 = 0.$$

Putting in the numbers and solving for X yields

$$16.2\,X^2 - 2.4\,X - 0.694 = 0 \;\rightarrow\; X = 0.29 \text{ m}$$ Ans.

CHAPTER 22

22-4

Let the final temperature be T. If $T > 0°C$ we must have

$$(100\text{ g})(0.5\text{ cal/g}\cdot C°)(15\text{ C°}) + (100\text{ g})(80\text{ cal/g}) + (100\text{ g})(1\text{ cal/g}\cdot C°)T = (200\text{ g})(1\text{ cal/g}\cdot C°)(25 - T)C°.$$

However, in solving this we find $T < 0°C$. Now try $T = 0°C$; in this case the heat lost by the water is (200 g)(1 cal/g·C°)(25 C°) = 5000 cal. 750 cal are required to bring the ice to 0°C and 8000 cal to melt all of it. Thus we conclude that T = 0°C Ans, and that not all of the ice melts.

22-6

If the area of the ring is a and the cross-sectional area of the sphere is A then

$$\Delta A = 2\alpha_A A(100 - T),\ \Delta a = 2\alpha_c a T,$$

T being the equilibrium temperature. We want

$$A - \Delta A = a + \Delta a \rightarrow T = \frac{A(1 - 200\alpha_A) - a}{2(a\alpha_c - A\alpha_A)} = 50.36°C.$$

The heat transferred was

$$\Delta Q = m_A c_A(100 - 50.36) = m_a c_a(50.36 - 0).$$

Substitute numerical values for the specific heats c_A and c_a to find

$$m_a/m_A = (0.215/0.0923)(49.64/50.36) = 2.296,$$

$$m_A/m_a = 0.44 \text{ Ans.}$$

22-14

Convert the temperatures to Celsius:

$$-20°F = -28.9°C, \quad 72°F = 22.2°C.$$

(a) Since $k_{glass} = 0.837$ W/m·C° we have a heat loss of

$$\frac{dQ}{dt} = (0.837 \text{ W/m·C°})(1 \text{ m}^2)\frac{22.2 + 28.9}{0.003}\frac{°C}{m} = 1.4 \times 10^4 \text{ W} \quad \underline{\text{Ans}}$$

for each square meter of the pane.

(b) The conductivity of air is 0.02386 W/m·C° so that for the storm window with two panes of glass,

$$\frac{dQ}{dt} = (1 \text{ m}^2)(22.2 + 28.9)C/(0.006/0.837 + 0.075/0.02386) = 16 \text{ W} \quad \underline{\text{Ans}}$$

for each square meter.

22-15

Consider a section of the ice with a cross-sectional area of 1 cm^2. Since its thickness is 5 cm the rate at which heat flows through it will be

$$\frac{dQ}{dt} = kA\frac{dT}{dx} = (0.004 \text{ cal/cm·s·C°})(1 \text{ cm}^2)\frac{-(-10°C - 0°C)}{5 \text{ cm}},$$

$$\frac{dQ}{dt} = 0.008 \text{ cal/s}.$$

Therefore it takes (80 cal/g)/(0.008 cal/s) = 10^4 s to freeze 1 g of water at 0°C. Hence in 10^4 s the layer of ice will grow by x cm where x is given from

$$(0.92 \text{ g/cm}^3)(1 \text{ cm}^2)(x \text{ cm}) = 1 \text{ g} \rightarrow x = 1.087 \text{ cm, per } 10^4 \text{ s}.$$

The hourly growth rate y will be then

$$y = \frac{3600 \text{ s}}{10{,}000 \text{ s}}(1.087 \text{ cm}) = 0.39 \text{ cm/h} \quad \underline{\text{Ans}}.$$

22-16

Assume $T_1 > T_2$ with $r_1 < r_2$. In a steady state

$$\frac{dQ}{dt} = - kA \frac{dT}{dr}$$

will be a constant, H say, for all r. With $A = 4\pi r^2$ we have

$$H = - k\, 4\pi r^2 \frac{dT}{dr} \rightarrow H \int_{r_1}^{r_2} \frac{dr}{r^2} = - 4\pi k \int_{T_1}^{T_2} dT ,$$

$$H = \frac{dQ}{dt} = 4\pi k(T_1 - T_2) \frac{r_1 r_2}{r_2 - r_1} \quad \underline{\text{Ans.}}$$

22-25

The work W done by friction is

$$W = \Delta K = \frac{1}{2} m_i v_i^2 - 0 = \frac{1}{2}(50 \text{ kg})(5.38 \text{ m/s})^2 = 723.61 \text{ J}$$

which is 172.86 cal. Since it takes 80 cal to melt 1 g of ice, the mass of ice melted will be

$$(172.86 \text{ cal})/(80 \text{ cal/g}) = 2.16 \text{ g} \quad \underline{\text{Ans.}}$$

22-30

In one-half liter of water are 500 g of water. To boil the water we must bring it to 100°C starting at 59°F = 15°C. The heat required to do this is

$$Q = m\, c\, \Delta T = (500 \text{ g})(1 \text{ cal/g}\cdot\text{C°})(100 - 15)\text{C°} = 42{,}500 \text{ cal.}$$

If we supply any additional heat the water will begin to vaporize. Now each shake produces

$$(0.5 \text{ kg})(9.8 \text{ m/s}^2)(0.3 \text{ m}) = 1.47 \text{ J}$$

of energy or 0.35 cal of heat. Therefore we need 42,500/0.35 =

1.21×10^5 shakes. At the rate of 30 shakes/min = $\frac{1}{2}$ shake per second it will take

$$2.42 \times 10^5 \text{ s} = 2.8 \text{ days } \underline{\text{Ans}},$$

to bring the water to the boiling point.

22-33

The first law of thermodynamics says that

$$Q = \Delta U + W.$$

Over a complete cycle $\Delta U = 0$ and therefore

$$W = Q = -(100 \text{ g})(80 \text{ cal/g}) = -8000 \text{ cal},$$

negative since heat left the gas. W is the work done by the gas and therefore the work done on the gas is + 8000 cal Ans.

22-35

(a) The actual time that the ball is in contact with the floor is very short so that unless the floor is extraordinarily hot no heat will have been added: $Q = 0$ Ans.

(b) By assumption $\Delta U > 0$ so that, by the first law $Q = \Delta U + W$, with $Q = 0$ we find $W < 0$ indicating that work has been done on the ball. The answer to the question, then, is yes.

(c) The change in internal energy ΔU is just the loss of mechanical energy which, if m is the mass of the ball, will be

$$\Delta U = mg\,\Delta h = m(9.8 \text{ m/s}^2)(9.5 \text{ m}) = 93 \text{ m J}$$

or 93 J/kg Ans.

(d) The rise in temperature ΔT is

$$\Delta T = \frac{\Delta U}{m\,c_p} = (93 \text{ m J})/(m)(0.12 \text{ cal/g}\cdot\text{C}^\circ)(4.19 \text{ J/cal}) = 0.20 \text{ C}^\circ \; \underline{\text{Ans}},$$

recalling that $1 \text{ g} = 10^{-3}$ kg.

22-36

Let

ρ = density of steam, V = volume of chamber

m = mass of steam, M, A = mass and area of piston,

V' = volume of steam, v = speed of piston.

(a) Although $V' \neq V$ we still have

$$\frac{dV'}{dt} = \frac{dV}{dt} = Av = \frac{d}{dt}\left(\frac{m}{\rho}\right) = \frac{1}{\rho}\frac{dm}{dt} \rightarrow \frac{dm}{dt} = \rho Av = (0.0006)(2)(0.3) \text{ g/s}$$

$$\frac{dm}{dt} = 3.6 \text{ X } 10^{-7} \text{ kg/s } \underline{\text{Ans.}}$$

(b) Differentiate the first law to obtain

$$\frac{dQ}{dt} = \frac{dU}{dt} + \frac{dW}{dt}.$$

We can evaluate two terms directly:

$$\frac{dW}{dt} = - p\frac{dV}{dt} = - pAv = - Mgv = - (2 \text{ kg})(9.8 \text{ m/s}^2)(0.003 \text{ m/s}),$$

$$\frac{dW}{dt} = - 0.0588 \text{ J/s};$$

$$\frac{dQ}{dt} = - \frac{dm}{dt}(540 \text{ cal/g}) = - (3.6 \text{ X } 10^{-4} \text{ g/s})(540 \text{ cal/g}),$$

$$\frac{dQ}{dt} = - 0.8138 \text{ J/s}.$$

Therefore

$$\frac{dU}{dt} = - 0.8138 - (- 0.0588) = - 0.755 \text{ J/s } \underline{\text{Ans.}}$$

(c) From (b)

$$\left|\frac{dQ}{dt}\right| = 0.81 \text{ J/s } \underline{\text{Ans.}}$$

23-11

Let l refer to the left arm and r to the right. Since the temperature does not change

$$p_{lf}V_{lf} = p_0V_{li} \rightarrow p_{lf} = p_0(V_{li}/V_{lf}) = \frac{50}{44}\,p_0;$$

similarly

$$p_{rf} = \frac{30}{26}\,p_0.$$

The mercury in the left column is 2 cm higher than in the right; we must have then

$$p_{lf} + \rho gh = p_{rf}.$$

With $\rho = 13.6 \times 10^3$ kg/m^3, $g = 9.8$ m/s^2 and $h = 0.02$ m we find that $\rho gh = 2666$ Pa. The preceding equation then yields

$$\frac{50}{44}\,p_0 + 2666\text{ Pa} = \frac{30}{26}\,p_0 \rightarrow p_0 = 1.5 \times 10^5\text{ Pa } \underline{\text{Ans.}}$$

23-12

The initial pressure is $p_i = 14.7 + 15 = 29.7$ lb/in^2. On expansion, with T constant,

$$p_iV_i = p_fV_f \rightarrow (29.7\text{ lb/in}^2)(5\text{ ft}^3) = (14.7\text{ lb/in}^2)\,V_f,$$

$$V_f = 10.1\text{ ft}^3.$$

The work done during this phase is

$$W_e = \int p\,dV = nRT\ln(V_f/V_i) = p_iV_i\ln(V_f/V_i) = (29.7)(5)\ln(10.1/5),$$

$$W_e = 104.4 \text{ lb}\cdot\text{ft}^3/\text{in}^2.$$

On compression at constant pressure,

$$W_c = p_f(V_i - V_f) = (14.7 \text{ lb/in}^2)(5 - 10.1) \text{ ft}^3 = -74.97,$$

the units being $\text{lb}\cdot\text{ft}^3/\text{in}^2$. Thus the total work done is

$$W = W_e - W_c = 104.4 - 74.97 = 29.44 \text{ lb}\cdot\text{ft}^3/\text{in}^2 = 4200 \text{ ft lb} \underline{\text{ Ans.}}$$

23-13

The momentum imparted to the wall on each collision is

$$\Delta p = \Delta(mv) = 2\,m\,v_\perp = 2mv\cos 45°.$$

If there are n collisions each second the pressure exerted on the wall is

$$P = \frac{F}{A} = n\,\frac{2\,m\,v_\perp}{A} = \frac{2\,m\,n\,v\cos 45°}{A},$$

$$P = 2(3.32 \times 10^{-24} \text{ g})(10^{23} \text{ s}^{-1})(10^5 \text{ cm/s})(0.707)/(2.0 \text{ cm}^2)$$

$$= 2.347 \times 10^4 \text{ dyne/cm}^2,$$

$$P = 2300 \text{ Pa} \underline{\text{ Ans.}}$$

23-21

The escape and root-mean-square speeds are

$$v_e = \sqrt{\frac{2\,G\,M}{R}} = \sqrt{2\,g\,R},\quad v_{rms} = \sqrt{\frac{3\,k\,T}{m}},$$

R being the radius of the planet. If these speeds are equal then

$$T = \frac{2}{3}\,\frac{g\,m\,R}{k}.$$

(a) For the earth R = 6400 km and we find

$$T = 1.0 \times 10^4 \text{ K for } H_2,\ 1.6 \times 10^5 \text{ K for } O_2 \quad \underline{\text{Ans.}}$$

(b) On the moon $g = 0.16(9.8\ m/s^2)$ and $R = 1.74 \times 10^6$ m. The equation for T gives in this case

$$T = 440\ K \text{ for } H_2,\ 7000\ K \text{ for } O_2 \ \underline{\text{Ans.}}$$

(c) From (a) we expect to find less H_2 than O_2 Ans.

23-24

(a) We know that

$$n = N_0/M = 6.02 \times 10^{23}\ /18\ g.$$

Then

$$\epsilon = (540\ cal/g)/(6.02 \times 10^{23}\ /18\ g^{-1}) = 6.8 \times 10^{-20}\ J \ \underline{\text{Ans.}}$$

(b) The average kinetic energy of a molecule is

$$K = \frac{3}{2}\ kT = \frac{3}{2}(1.38 \times 10^{-23}\ J/K)(300\ K) = 0.62 \times 10^{-20}\ J.$$

Thus $\epsilon/K = 11$ Ans.

23-33

The speed of sound is

$$v = \sqrt{\frac{\gamma\ p}{\rho}}\ ;$$

but the equation of state is

$$p = \frac{k}{m}\rho T$$

so that

$$v = \sqrt{\gamma\ \frac{k\ T}{m}}\ ,$$

independent of p and ρ.

23-35

From problem 23-33 we have

$$v = \sqrt{\gamma \frac{k\,T}{m}}\ .$$

Taking differentials,

$$\Delta v = \frac{1}{2}\, v\, \frac{\Delta T}{T} = \frac{1}{2}\,(331\ \text{m/s})\ \frac{1\text{K}}{273\ \text{K}} = 0.61\ \text{m/s}\ \underline{\text{Ans}},$$

the Kelvin degree interval being the same as the Celsius.

23-38

We use the adiabatic equation of state

$$p_1 V_1{}^{\gamma} = p_2 V_2{}^{\gamma}.$$

(a) With volumes in liters,

$$p_1(1)^{3/2} = (1\ \text{atm})(4)^{3/2} \ \rightarrow\ p_1 = 4^{3/2} = 8.0\ \text{atm}\ \underline{\text{Ans}}.$$

(b) For an ideal gas pV = nRT so that

$$p_1/p_2 = (T_1/T_2)(V_2/V_1).$$

Combine this with the equation of the adiabat to obtain

$$T_1 = T_2(V_2/V_1)^{\gamma-1} = (300\ \text{K})(4/1)^{1.5-1} = 600\ \text{K}\ \underline{\text{Ans}}.$$

23-41

The constant pressure expansion is easily plotted on a p-V diagram shown on the next page.

For T constant we have

$$p_0 V_0 = n\ RT = p_1 V_1$$

so that

$$p_1 = p_0 V_0 / V_1,$$

the graph of the isotherm being a hyperbola.
For the adiabatic process $Q = 0$.
Also pV^{γ} = constant and therefore

$$p_1' = p_0(V_0/V_1)^{\gamma}.$$

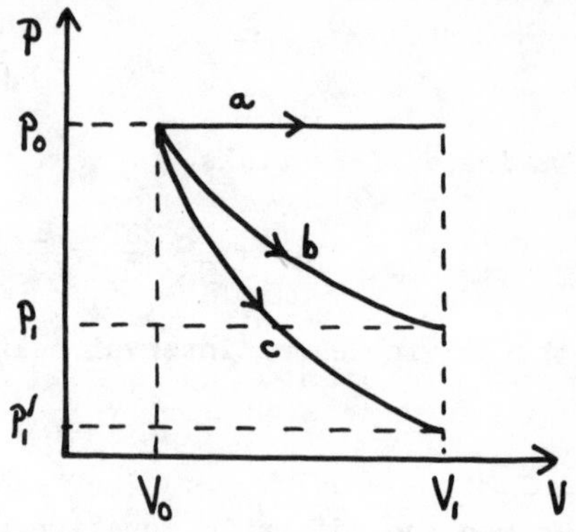

But $\gamma > 1$ and $V_1 > V_0$ so that $p_1 > p_1'$. Hence the curves are positioned as shown. Now recall that the areas under these curves equals the work done during the respective process. Hence we can immediately order the works.
For an ideal gas ΔU is proportional to ΔT. Since $pV = nRT$ the expansion at constant pressure is accompanied by a rise in temperature. For the adiabatic process we conclude from the first law $Q = \Delta U + W$ that since $Q = 0$ and $W > 0$, ΔU and ΔT must be less than zero. We conclude that for the constant pressure process the change in internal energy and the work done must be greater than for the other processes and for the adiabatic process they must be least. From the first law Q must be greatest for the former process and least for the latter.

<u>23-42</u>

The numerical values needed in this problem are

$p_0 = 1.013 \times 10^5$ Pa, $\quad g = 9.8$ m/s^2,
$a = 0.45$ m, $\quad h = 0.1$ m.
$\rho = 13.6 \times 10^3$ kg/m^3,

Also let A be the cross-sectional area of the tube.
(a) Isothermal case. If the mercury drops a distance x then

$$p_b = p_t + \rho gh.$$

The isothermal condition yields

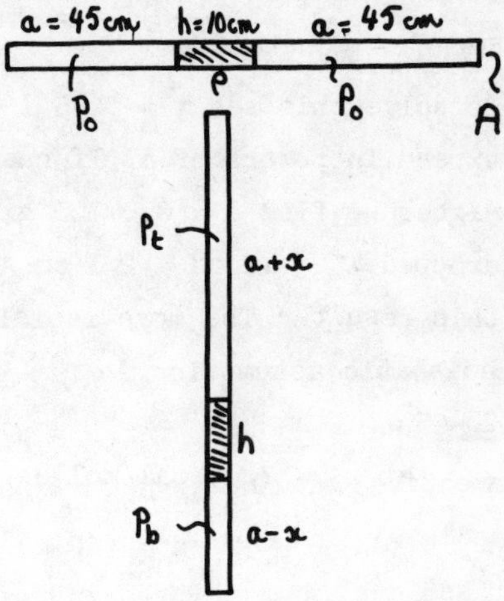

$$pV = \text{constant},$$

$$p_b(a - x)A = p_0 aA,$$

$$p_t(a + x)A = p_0 aA.$$

Solve these equations for p_b, p_t and substitute into the first equation to obtain

$$\frac{p_0 a}{a - x} = \frac{p_0 a}{a + x} + \rho gh,$$

$$x^2 + \frac{2\,p_0 a}{\rho gh}\,x - a^2 = 0,$$

$$x^2 + 6.84\,x - 0.2025 = 0 \;\rightarrow\; x = 0.0295 = 2.95 \text{ cm } \underline{\text{Ans.}}$$

(b) Adiabatic case. Note the change in notation. We still have

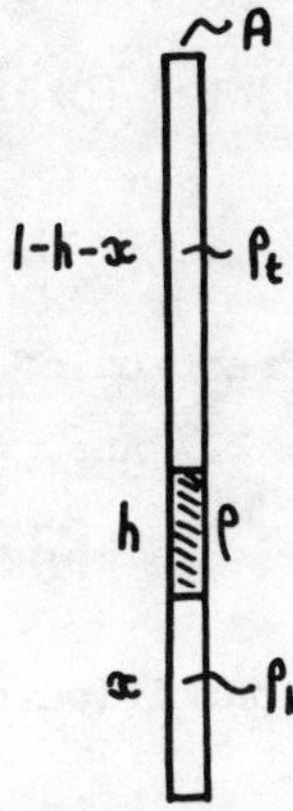

$$p_b = p_t + \rho gh.$$

From the adiabatic condition,

$$p_b(xA)^\gamma = p_0(aA)^\gamma \;\rightarrow\; p_b = p_0\left(\frac{a}{x}\right)^\gamma.$$

Similarly,

$$p_t = p_0\left(\frac{a}{l - h - x}\right)^\gamma.$$

Substitute these into the first equation and put in numerical values to get

$$\left(\frac{a}{x}\right)^\gamma = \frac{\rho gh}{p_0} + \left(\frac{a}{l - h - x}\right)^\gamma,$$

$$\left(\frac{0.45}{x}\right)^{1.4} = 0.1316 + \left(\frac{0.45}{0.9 - x}\right)^{1.4}.$$

To solve this set $x = 0.45(1 - \Delta)$, put this into the equation and expand in powers of Δ. If quadratic terms are retained but none higher we find $\Delta = 0.04703$ giving $x = 0.4288$ m. Thus the mercury dropped $45 - 42.88 = 2.1$ cm Ans. (Linear terms in Δ will also give this result.) The more rapidly the tube is turned the better the adiabatic assumption.

23-45

(a) Let $c_p = 7.03$ cal/mol be the molar specific heat. We have

$$n = (10\text{ g})/(32\text{ g/mol}) = 0.3125\text{ mol}$$

of oxygen present and the temperature change is $\Delta T = 100$ C°. Thus

$$Q = (0.3125\text{ mol})(7.03\text{ cal/mol})(100) = 219.7\text{ cal} = 920\text{ J Ans.}$$

(b) Since oxygen is diatomic,

$$\Delta U = n(\tfrac{5}{2}R)\Delta T = (0.3125\text{ mol})\,\tfrac{5}{2}\,(8.314\text{ J/mol}\cdot\text{K})(100\text{ K})$$

$$\Delta U = 649.5\text{ J}.$$

Hence the fraction of heat used to raise the internal energy is $649.5/920 = 71\%$ Ans.

23-47

By the equipartition of energy theorem

$$\frac{1}{2}m\overline{v^2} = \frac{3}{2}kT.$$

We also have, from kinetic theory,

$$p = \frac{1}{3}\rho\overline{v^2}.$$

Combining these,

$$p = \frac{1}{3}\rho\frac{3kT}{m} = \frac{\rho}{m}\,kT = n_v kT$$

n_v being the number of particles per unit volume. Therefore, if P and T are given the number of molecules in any volume is uniquely determined.

23-48

Let V be the volume of the room and n the number of molecules per unit volume in the air. Since the pressure remains unchanged,

$$p_0 = n_1 kT_1 = n_2 kT_2.$$

The internal energy after heating is

$$U_2 = \frac{3}{2}(n_2 V)kT_2 = \frac{3}{2}\,V\,\left(\frac{n_1 kT_1}{kT_2}\right)kT_2 = \frac{3}{2}(n_1 V)kT_1 = U_1$$

the internal energy before heating. Of course, we have raised the temperature of the air.

23-53

A sudden compression is very likely adiabatic since there is little time for heat to flow. Therefore, by the solution to problem 23-38,

$$T_1 = T_2(V_2/V_1)^{\gamma-1}$$

(a) Monatomic gas: $\gamma = 5/3$. With $T_2 = 290$ K and $V_2 = 10\ V_1$ we find

$$T_1 = (290\text{ K})(10)^{2/3} = 1350\text{ K}$$ Ans.

(b) Diatomic gas: $\gamma = 7/5$. With the other data unchanged we get

$$T_1 = 730\text{ K}$$ Ans.

24-4

The number of jelly beans per unit volume n is

$$n = 15/(1000\ \text{cm}^3) = 1.5 \times 10^{-2}\ \text{cm}^{-3},$$

and the diameter d of a jelly bean is d = 1.0 cm. Hence the mean free path L will be given by

$$L^{-1} = \pi\sqrt{2}\ (1.5 \times 10^{-3}\ \text{cm}^{-3})(1.0\ \text{cm})^2 \rightarrow L = 15\ \text{cm}\ \underline{\text{Ans.}}$$

24-7

(a) The root-mean-square speed is

$$v_{rms} = \sqrt{\frac{3kT}{m}} = \sqrt{\frac{3(1.38 \times 10^{-23})(4000)}{2(1.66 \times 10^{-27})}} = 7.1\ \text{km/s}\ \underline{\text{Ans.}}$$

(b) When they touch,

$$d = r_H + r_A = \tfrac{1}{2}(10^{-8} + 3 \times 10^{-8}) = 2.0 \times 10^{-8}\ \text{cm}\ \ \underline{\text{Ans.}}$$

(c) By definition of mean free path the collision frequency is

$$\frac{v}{L} = \sqrt{2}\ n_A \pi d^2 v_{rms} = \sqrt{2}(4 \times 10^{-19})\pi(2 \times 10^{-8})(7.1 \times 10^5)\ s^{-1},$$

$$\text{collision frequency} = 5 \times 10^{10}\ s^{-1}\ \underline{\text{Ans.}}$$

24-8

Consider a group n_0 of particles at some instant and let any molecule that suffers a collision be removed from the group. Let n be the number of particles still in the group after each has traveled a distance x. We assume that the number dn of particles lost from the group as each molecule travels dx is

$$dn = -P\,n\,dx, \quad n = n(x),$$

where P is a constant. Then

$$\frac{dn}{n} = -P\,dx \quad \rightarrow \quad n = n_0 e^{-Px}.$$

Thus the probability that any molecule travels x without a collision is n/n_0: i.e.

$$\text{Prob.} = e^{-Px}.$$

The mean free path L is

$$L = \int x\,dn \Big/ \int dn,$$

since dn = the number of particles that have survived a distance x but do not survive a distance x + dx: i.e. dn is the number of particles whose mean free path is x:

$$L = \int_0^\infty x(-P\,n_0 e^{-Px})dx \Big/ \int_0^\infty(-P\,n_0 e^{-Px})\,dx = \frac{1}{P},$$

and therefore

$$\text{Prob.} = e^{-x/L} \quad \underline{\text{Ans.}}$$

<u>24-13</u>

(a) By definition,

$$N\bar{v} = v_1 + v_2 + \ldots v_N, \quad Nv_{rms}^2 = v_1^2 + v_2^2 + \ldots v_N^2.$$

For any particle,

$$v_i = \bar{v} + (v_i - \bar{v}) = \bar{v} + \delta_i.$$

Thus

$$Nv_{rms}^2 = (\bar{v} + \delta_1)^2 + (\bar{v} + \delta_2)^2 + \ldots (\bar{v} + \delta_N)^2$$

$$Nv_{rms}^2 = N\,\bar{v}^2 + 2\,\bar{v}\sum\delta_i + \sum\delta_i^{\,2}.$$

But

$$\sum\delta_i = \sum(v_i - \bar{v}) = \sum v_i - N\,\bar{v} = N\,\bar{v} - N\,\bar{v} = 0$$

Thus

$$v_{rms}^2 = \bar{v}^2 + \frac{1}{N}\sum\delta_i^{\,2}.$$

Since $\delta_i^{\,2} \geqslant 0$ we have $v_{rms} \geqslant \bar{v}$.

(b) If all the $\delta_i = 0$, $v_{rms} = \bar{v}$: all speeds are the same Ans.

24-14

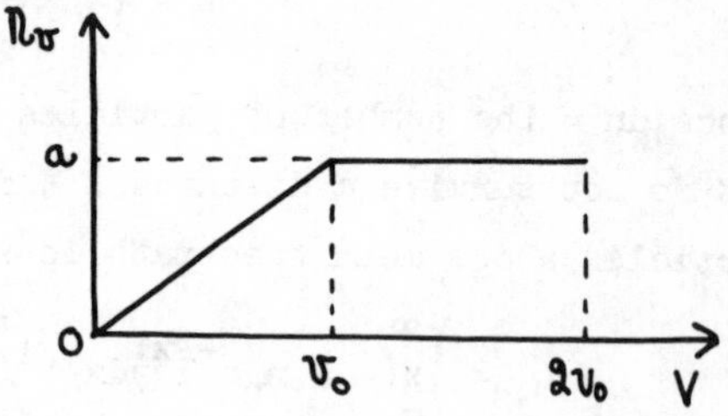

(a) The area under the curve is just the number of particles:

$$N = \frac{1}{2}\,v_0 a + v_0 a,$$

$$a = \frac{2}{3}\,N/v_0 \quad \text{Ans.}$$

(b) The area under the curve between $v = 1.5v_0$ and $2v_0$ is

$$\frac{1}{2}\,v_0 a = \frac{1}{2}\,v_0\,\frac{2}{3}\,N/v_0 = \frac{N}{3} \quad \text{Ans.}$$

(c) By definition,

$$v = \frac{1}{N}\int v\,N_v\,dv = \frac{1}{N}\int_0^{v_0} v\left(\frac{a}{v_0}\right)dv + \frac{1}{N}\int_{v_0}^{2v_0} a\,v\,dv = \frac{11}{9}\,v_0 \quad \text{Ans.}$$

24-20

(a) By equipartition of energy

$$\frac{1}{2}\,M\bar{v}^2 = \frac{3}{2}\,kT.$$

But the mass M of the grain is

$$M = \frac{4}{3}\pi R^3 = \frac{4}{3}\pi(2 \times 10^{-6}\ \text{cm})^3(1\ \text{g/cm}^3) = 3.351 \times 10^{-17}\ \text{g},$$

and therefore

$$v_{rms} = \sqrt{\frac{3kT}{m}} = \sqrt{\frac{3(1.38 \times 10^{-16})(100)}{3.351 \times 10^{-17}}} = 35\ \text{cm/s}\ \underline{\text{Ans.}}$$

(b) Again the equipartition theorem requires

$$\frac{1}{2} I\omega^2 = \frac{3}{2} kT.$$

Since

$$I = \frac{2}{5} MR^2 = \frac{2}{5}(3.351 \times 10^{-17}\ \text{g})(2 \times 10^{-6}\ \text{cm})^2 = 5.36 \times 10^{-29}$$

the units being $g\cdot cm^2$. The angular frequency becomes

$$\omega = \sqrt{\frac{3kT}{I}} = 2.78 \times 10^7\ \text{rad/s}$$

so that

$$\nu = \omega/2\pi = 4.4 \times 10^6\ \text{s}^{-1}\ \underline{\text{Ans.}}$$

<u>24-26</u>

Van der Waal's equation is

$$(P + \frac{n^2 a}{V^2})(\frac{V}{n} - b) = R\,T.$$

Now let

$$V = v_{cr}v = 3b\,v,\ P = p_{cr}p = \frac{a}{27\,b^2}\,p,\ T = T_{cr}t = \frac{8a}{27bR}\,t.$$

Substituting these gives

$$(\frac{a}{27\,b^2}\,p + \frac{n^2 a}{9b^2 v^2})(\frac{3bv}{n} - b) = R\,\frac{8a}{27bR}\,t,$$

$$\left(\frac{p}{3} + \frac{n^2}{v^2}\right)\left(3\,\frac{v}{n} - 1\right) = \frac{8}{3}\,t,$$

independent of a and b.

CHAPTER 25

25-6

For a Carnot refrigerator,

$$T_1/T_2 = Q_1/Q_2 = (Q_2 + W)/Q_2 \rightarrow W = Q_2 \frac{T_1 - T_2}{T_2}.$$

(a) $T_1 = 27°C = 300\ K$, $T_2 = 7°C = 280\ K$. Therefore

$$W = (1\ J)\frac{300\ K - 280\ K}{280\ K} = 0.071\ J\ \underline{Ans.}$$

(b) $T_2 = 200\ K$:

$$W = (1\ J)\frac{300\ K - 200\ K}{200\ K} = 0.50\ J\ \underline{Ans.}$$

(c) $T_2 = 100\ K$:

$$W = (1\ J)\frac{300\ K - 100\ K}{100\ K} = 2.0\ J\ \underline{Ans.}$$

(d) $T_2 = 50\ K$:

$$W = (1\ J)\frac{300\ K - 50\ K}{50\ K} = 5.0\ J\ \underline{Ans.}$$

25-13

(a)

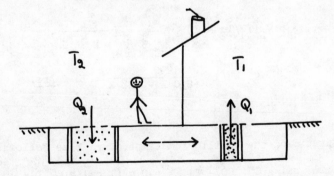

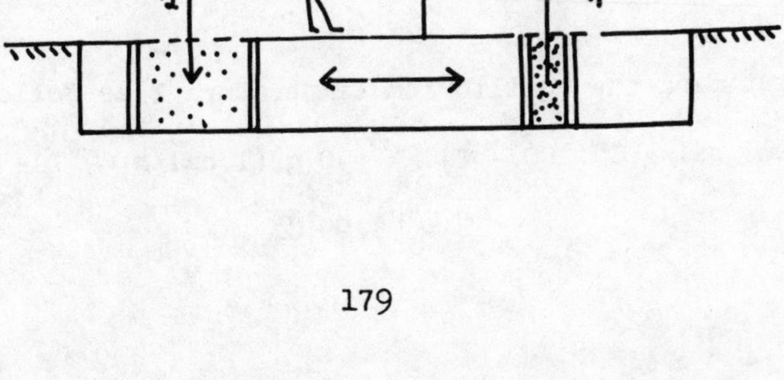

(b) First let the gas in the pump expand so that the gas temperature is decreased and lower than the outside temperature T_2. Therefore a quantity of heat Q_2 is extracted from the outside atmosphere at T_2. Then move the piston into the house and compress the gas until its temperature is higher than inside the house at T_1. A larger quantity of heat Q_1 is delivered to the inside of the house. Thus, in principle, there is no significant difference between the heat pump and the refrigerator. In practical use, for a refrigerator a a quantity of heat Q_2 is extracted at T_2 through the vaporization of a liquid instead of the expansion of a gas in the heat pump.

(c) By the first law

$$Q_1 = Q_2 + W$$

the change in internal energy being zero over one cycle.

(d) The heat pump can be reversed by reversing the expansion and compression stages.

(e) The advantages are that Q_1, the heat delivered, is greater than W, the energy paid for (to the power company), and that the pump can be operated to heat and cool.

<u>25-14</u>

The system operates like a refrigerator so we have

$$W + Q_2 = Q_1, \; W = Q_2(T_1/T_2 - 1) \;\rightarrow\; Q_1 = W\frac{T_1}{T_1 - T_2},$$

$$Q_1 = (1\ \text{J})\frac{290\ \text{K}}{290\ \text{K} - 268\ \text{K}} = 13\ \text{J}\ \underline{\text{Ans.}}$$

<u>25-20</u>

We must first find the equilibrium temperature T as follows:

$$(200\ \text{g})(0.215\ \text{cal/g}\cdot\text{C}^\circ)(100 - T)\text{C}^\circ = (50\ \text{g})(1\ \text{cal/g}\cdot\text{C}^\circ)(T - 20)\text{C}^\circ,$$

$$T = 56.99^\circ\text{C}.$$

This is T = 330.14 K. The total entropy change is then

$$\Delta S = \Delta S_{water} + \Delta S_{al},$$

$$\Delta S = (50\text{ g})(1\text{ cal/g}\cdot\text{C°})\ln\frac{330.14}{293.15} - (200\text{g})(0.215\text{ cal/g}\cdot\text{K})\ln\frac{373.15}{330.14},$$

$$\Delta S = 5.933 - 5.255 = +\ 0.68\text{ cal/K } \underline{\text{Ans.}}$$

<u>25-22</u>

Clearly the equilibrium temperature is the temperature of the lake which is 15°C = 288.15 K. The entropy changes are the following.

$$\Delta S_{ice} = (10\text{ g})(0.52\text{ cal/g}\cdot\text{C°})\ln\frac{273.15}{263.15} = 0.1939\text{ cal/K.}$$

$$\Delta S_{ice\to water} = (10\text{ g})(79.6\text{ cal/g})/(273.15\text{ K}) = 2.9141\text{ cal/K.}$$

$$\Delta S_{water} = (10\text{ g})(1.0\text{ cal/g}\cdot\text{K})\ln\frac{288.15}{273.15} = 0.5345\text{ cal/K.}$$

$$\Delta S_{lake} = \Delta Q/T_{lake}.$$

The heat ΔQ transferred is

$$-\ \Delta Q = (10\text{ g})(0.52\text{ cal/g}\cdot\text{K})(10\text{ K}) + (10\text{ g})(79.6\text{ cal/g}) + (10\text{ g})(1\text{ cal/g}\cdot\text{K})(15\text{ K});$$

with T_{lake} = 288.15 K we find

$$\Delta S_{lake} = -\ 3.4635\text{ cal/K.}$$

Adding all the entropy changes gives

$$\Delta S_{total} = +\ 0.18\text{ cal/K } \underline{\text{Ans.}}$$

<u>25-27</u>

For the object,

$$dS = \frac{dQ}{T} = \frac{C\ dT}{T}\ ;\ \Delta S = \int_{T_i}^{T_f}\frac{C}{T}\,dT;\ \Delta S = \text{area under curve of } \frac{C}{T} \text{ vs T.}$$

For the reservoir,

$$\Delta S = -\frac{Q}{T_f} = -\frac{C(T_f - T_i)}{T_f} = -\text{ (area of rectangle under curve on C/T vs T plot).}$$

Hence the total entropy change is the shaded area below.

(a)

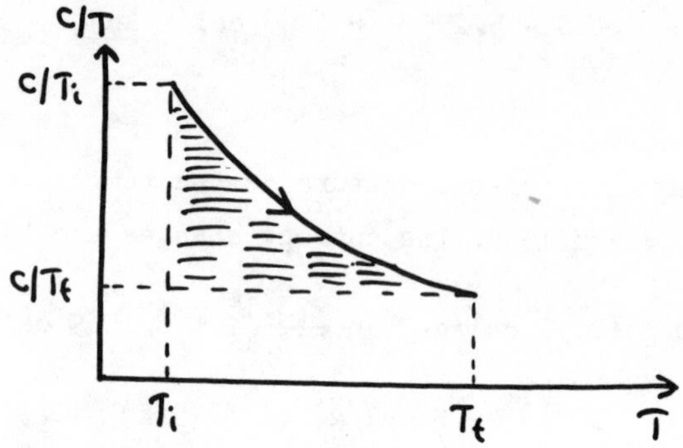

(b) Consider, for example, heating the object in two stages. Clearly the area to the right is less than the area above.

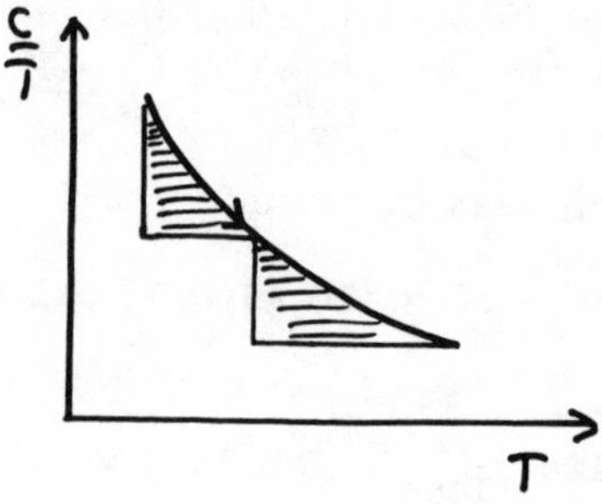

25-28

Infinitesimal cycles implies reversible processes. Also, for W_{max}, we use Carnot engines.

(a) If Q_r is the heat delivered to the reservoir at T_1,

$$W = Q - Q_r$$

so that the entropy change of the reservoir is

$$\Delta S_r = +\frac{Q_r}{T_1} .$$

But if ΔS_b is the entropy change of the body $\Delta S_r + \Delta S_b = 0$ and then

$$W = W_{max} = Q - T_1\Delta S_r = Q + T_1\Delta S_b = Q + T_1(S_1 - S_2),$$

$$W_{max} = Q - T_1(S_2 - S_1) \text{ \underline{Ans.}}$$

(b) Similarly, if Q_d is the heat delivered to the reservoir at T_1,

$$W = Q_d - Q = T_1\Delta S_r - Q = T_1(-\Delta S_b) - Q = -(S_0 - S_1)T_1 - Q,$$

$$W_{max} = T_1(S_1 - S_0) - Q \text{ \underline{Ans.}}$$

<u>25-30</u>

(a) The probability P of dealing any one hand is

$$P = 1/(\text{number of hands that can be dealt}).$$

The number of hands that can be dealt is

$$\frac{52!}{13!\,(52 - 13)!} = 0.635 \times 10^{12}.$$

Thus $w_i = 1.57 \times 10^{-12}$. The initial entropy is then

$$S_i = k \ln w_i = (1.38 \times 10^{-23} \text{ J/K}) \ln(1.57 \times 10^{-12})/(4.186 \text{ J/cal}),$$

$$S_i = 9.0 \times 10^{-23} \text{ cal/K}.$$

The final entropy is

$$S_f = k \ln(1) = 0,$$

Thus the entropy change is $\Delta S = -9.0 \times 10^{-23}$ cal/K <u>Ans.</u>

(b) From previous problems and examples in the text we see that this is much smaller than thermodynamic entropy changes.

(c) [illegible] is the entropy change of the body [illegible] = 0 and then

[illegible]

(d) Similarly, [illegible] is the heat delivered to the reservoir at

[illegible]

(e) The probability [illegible] one has

[illegible] that can be [illegible]

another [illegible] that can be [illegible]

[illegible]

The [illegible] initial [illegible] is then

[illegible]

The [illegible] entropy is

[illegible]

Thus the entropy change [illegible] = 0.2305 [illegible] units.

If from previous problems and examples in the text we see that

this is much smaller than the reservoir's entropy change.